Chicago

Editor: Daphne Christensen
Design: Gerald Kalvelage

Department of Public Works, City of Chicago
Room 406, City Hall, 121 North LaSalle St., Chicago, Illinois 60602
Printed by Rand McNally & Company, Chicago, Illinois 60680
Library of Congress Card Catalog Number 73-85375
Published 1973

Chicago Public Works: A History

Chicago

City of Chicago
Richard J. Daley
Mayor

Department of Public Works
Milton Pikarsky
Commissioner

RAND McNALLY & COMPANY
Chicago / New York / San Francisco

Contents

"I have found a city—a real city—and they call it Chicago."
Rudyard Kipling

Introduction

Chicago is a city that had to be. In spite of a physical environment intrinsically hostile to man, in spite of a harsh and unyielding climate, unparalleled population growth and disasters of staggering proportions, Chicago has endured. It is too fortunate a combination of inland sea, land and river routes. Chicago is said to be near the sources of things men need, and near the men who need them.

The environmental pollution which now threatens cities throughout the world arrived early in Chicago. The entire city had to be elevated some 10 feet with land-fill to provide adequate sewer drainage. When the lake became polluted from the draining sewage, vast underground tunnels were dug under the lake for fresh water. Finally, the river was made to flow backwards.

As we look back, it is difficult to realize that so much has changed in a scant hundred years. Yet the technological triumphs of our time are no less impressive although different in style. Today, with the sweeping technological advances in every field, our accomplishments grow from the interdisciplinary cooperation of specialists and generalists, working together as professionals for a common goal.

Some things remain with us. Chicago engineers learned the technique long ago of seeking out the best solutions for the most challenging problems, of resisting easy compromises which gave temporary relief and merely pushed the basic problem downstream for another generation to handle. Searching and perceptive, engineers learned to develop early insight and awareness as to what needed doing, and developed the persuasive powers to see the projects through to completion.

But more important than inspired engineering leadership has been the demonstrated ability of the people of Chicago to seek out the solutions to their problems. Not at all reluctant to pay the price for improving the quality of life, the people of Chicago have indebted the city through bond issues and themselves through tax assessments to finance improvements. This is the "I Will" spirit of Chicago, the spirit prevailing throughout public works, the spirit told in these chapters.

Chicago Public Works: A History

Chicago

Historical Background 1

Rush for Life,   October 9, 1871
*Chicago received the most devasting blow
ever delivered to a city by fire. The Great
Fire of 1871 became, in fact, a convenient
yardstick to measure other catastrophes.
Although no photographs of the fire
survived, an artist for Harpers Weekly was
stopping at the Sherman House the night
of the holocaust. Taking his sketch pads
with him when he fled under the river
through the Washington Street tunnel, he
drew this vivid scene of fleeing refugees at
the Randolph Street Bridge.*

3

The City of Chicago

Chicago is a unique, one-of-a-kind urban phenomenon. Perhaps no other city in the history of civilization was as well suited to the conditions of its time of birth and development. Born in the industrial revolution and synonymous with it, the name Chicago was soon known throughout the world as a bastion of economic and industrial strength characteristic of a dynamic, innovative civilization.

The name itself, Chicago, is said by some to stem from the Indian word for the wild North American leek which grew in abundance on the marshy plain before man came; similar to wild garlic or wild onion this odoriferous plant is found throughout the eastern half of the continent from Canada to the South. Others say Chicago, in practical Indian usage, meant strong or great, a term applied to the Mississippi River, to thunder or to the voice of the Great Manitou. Whatever the origin, Chicago has always been called Chicago, as no other place on earth.

More than any other city in the world, Chicago grew and was nurtured by engineering innovation and the soaring technical skills of the 19th century. With a growth in population unequaled by any region of the world, people came for opportunities denied them elsewhere. While some early visitors may have found the vast expanses of prairie impressive, or been stirred by the potential for a continuous waterway stretching from the Great Lakes to the Gulf of Mexico, it was the fast growing industrial facilities, immense both in terms of physical size and production capability, which captured the imaginations of the populace. Linked with these private technical feats were the public works projects, themselves often of staggering proportion. This is the story of some of those achievments.

1. Chicago, 1779
Chicago River's easily recognizable Y-shape is clearly visible in this early lithograph. The first resident, Jean Baptiste Point du Sable, built the cabin about 1779 and later sold the property to Jean Lalime sometime after 1804, it became John Kinzie's property. Kinzie killed Lalime during a fight following a dispute as to which would act as sutler for the Fort Dearborn garrison.

2. Construction of Fort Dearborn, 1803
The first public works in Chicago, the construction of Fort Dearborn, began in July of 1803, the year of the Louisiana Purchase. Under the direction of the company leader, Captain John Whistler, (grandfather of painter, James Whistler) the fort was built and named for General Dearborn, Secretary of War under President Jefferson.

3. First House, 1816
John Kinzie built this house about 1816, located near Michigan Avenue. The four Lombardy poplars, shady cottonwoods, and white picket fence were long a landmark for ships approaching Chicago.

4. Chicago, 1812
Based on a study by historian, Harry A. Musham, from a report by Captain Whistler, the drawing shows early Chicago. In 1834, very high river waters threatened to flood Fort Dearborn. The soldiers dug a cut through the sand bar, changing the course of the river as it is today.

All photographs are on file with the Chicago Historical Society

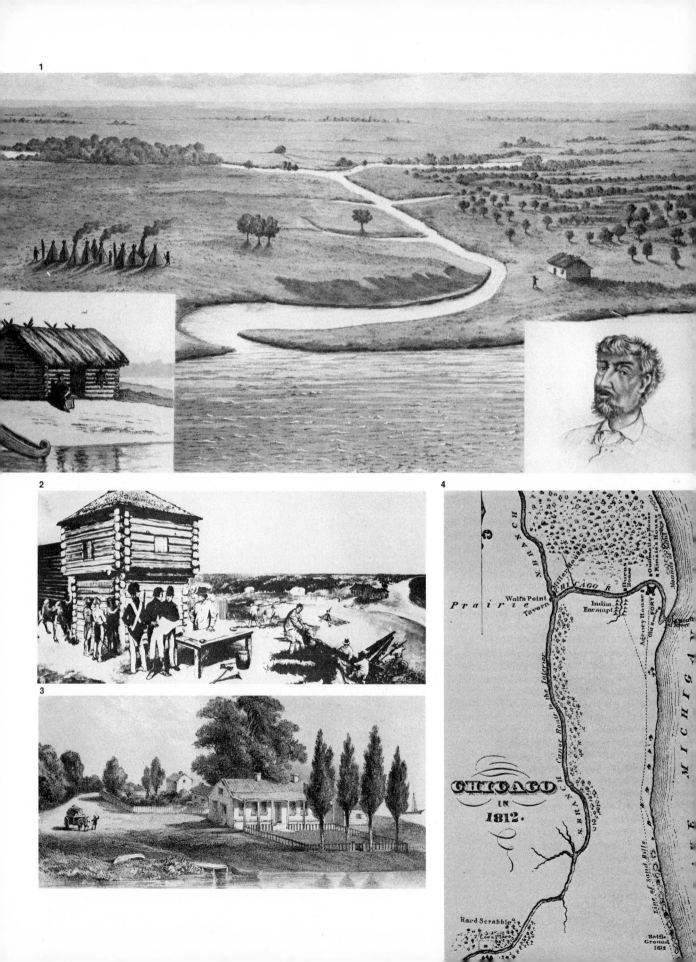

1

2

3

4

CHICAGO
IN
1812.

Prairie

Wolf's Point
Tavern

N. BRANCH

Miller House

CHICAGO R.

Indian
Encampt.

Agency House

Old Am. FORT

Kinzie House

Burns House

Ouilmette House

Mounds of Chicago

S. BRANCH

Canal Route to the Interior.

L A K E   M I C H I G A N

At Mouth of River

Line of sand hills

Hard Scrabble
Lee's Place

Battle
Ground
1812

A Difference of 300 Years

It would not be possible today to retrace the route traveled by the early explorers. Portions of the Chicago River have been filled in and no longer exist; the Beaver Lake which made a continuous waterway to the Mississippi in spring has been replaced by a year-round canal; land fill operations have extended the shoreline to the east and raised Chicago ten to twenty feet above grade.

Every school child is familiar with the 17th century explorers: Marquette, Joliet and LaSalle. Those of the 18th century are largely unknown to us until the arrival of Chicago's first permanent settler, Jean Baptiste Point DeSables, or DuSables, who built a cabin on the north bank of the river about 1779. His cabin site was about where the Equitable Building is today, some twenty feet below present-day Michigan Avenue.

These early adventurers would be astonished and bewildered at the sight along the river today: Entering the city from the west, or inland side, as did Marquette and Joliet, travelers today are greeted by a vast array of storage tanks for gas and petroleum, grain elevators and rolling mills in an area which was once a sylvan setting. Continuing along the south branch of the river, the buildings get taller and more numerous as the travelers pass remnants of Chicago's famed fast-crumbling roundhouses and abandoned factories, victims of the fast pace of technological change.

Nearing the Loop area and the junction of the main channel of the river, the traveler may become aware that the river is abnormally straight, without bends or twisting rivelets common in streams that meander through a marshy prairie chocked with bulrushes and cattails. Gone are the sloughs and marshes that aproned the main stream in earlier times, all replaced by concrete embankments crossed with movable bridge structures which open like jaws of a giant alligator, each jaw weighing hundreds of tons. Passing into the main branch of the Chicago River, now broader, deeper and straighter than in Joliet's time, the travelers pass through a concrete and steel canyon framed by dozens of towering buildings, and then directly into Lake Michigan through locks

5. The Chicago Portage, 1816
A treaty with the Chippewa, Ottawa, and Potawatami in 1816 resulted in the cessation to the United States of a ten-mile strip of land along the Chicago River. James Scharf, a devoted student of Indian lore, mapped the region showing trails, camps, and burial grounds in addition to waterways of interest to traders.

6. New Fort Dearborn, 1816
Settlers and traders ventured up the waterways once again under the protection of their little fort, built on the same high ground near the mouth of the river as the original fort (1803-1812). Today commemorative markers in the sidewalk on Michigan Avenue outline the site of the old Fort, torn down in 1857.

All photographs are on file with the Chicago Historical Society

Chicago Portage

BEING THE TERRITORY CEDED TO THE UNITED STATES GOVERNMENT
BY THE ALLIED TRIBES OF POTAWATAMI, CHIPPEWA AND OTTAWA INDIANS
BY TREATY OF PORTAGE DES SIOUX, MISSOURI IN AUGUST OF 1816.

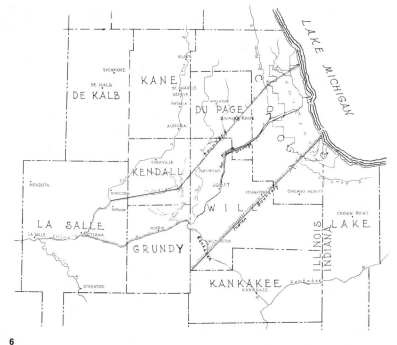

which stand at a river mouth once turned south by a great sandbar. Today at the river's mouth stands the 3,000 foot Navy Pier where ocean-going vessels moor, ships which could not have been sailed here in an earlier day before the building of the St. Lawrence Seaway.

Perhaps the most important difference in today's journey is a change nearly imperceptible to all but the trained mariner. . . . Today an easterly passage along the Chicago River takes the traveler upstream. Joliet, who traveled in the same direction, traveled downstream!

7

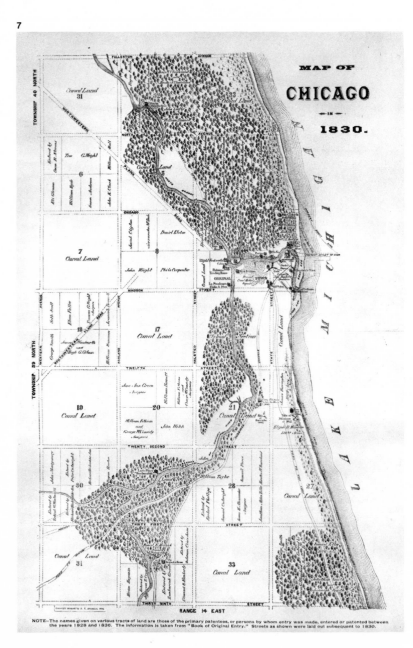

7. Map of Chicago, 1830
The radial system of planked roads converging near the Loop area is apparent in this early map. These roads followed Indian trails that were on ridges of higher ground of the moraines left by receding glaciers eons ago.

8. The Seal of Chicago
The seal represents the National spirit with the Indian as Aboriginal discoverer; a ship represents the white man's exploration and commerce, a sheaf of wheat is synonomous with cornucopia; the child in a pearl symbolizing the young city as a gem in the lake. The Motto: Urbs in Horto, City in a Garden.

9. Lighthouse, 1832
Abandoned Fort Dearborn stands beside a new lighthouse signaling the advent of heavy river traffic. In 1832, 70 bushels of wheat were shipped, over 2 million by mid-century, and by 1870 the figure reached 16 million.

10. McCormick Reaper and Mower Works, 1860
Built in 1847, the factory produced 700 machines and doubled this output by 1850. By 1868, 10,000 reapers were made annually. The black smoke polluting the environment has been colored-in to look darker than reality and typifying the Nineteenth Century attitude that smoke meant opportunity and growth. Note the multimodal water-rail-roadway transportation facilities.

All photographs are on file with the Chicago Historical Society

8

9

10

Engineering City Boundaries

When the Revolutionary War with England was concluded in 1783, the young nation moved quickly to expand toward the west. By 1800, settlers sprinkled the Chicago area and in 1803 the federal government built a small fort to offer a measure of protection and encouragement. Fort Dearborn, named for Jefferson's secretary of war, General Henry Dearborn, was abandoned in 1812 when hostilities again broke out with Britain over a dispute as to control of the American continent outside the colonial region. One of the first cruel acts of this brief war, which included the burning of Washington by a British expedition, was the massacre of these early Chicagoans at the hands of Indians armed and incited by the British: A grisly story well told in all Chicago history books.

The slaughter of Chicago's residents did not slow the pace of development but in one sense acted to accelerate it. The peace of 1814 made it unmistakably clear that the continent belonged to the American colonies and that any sacrifice would be made to maintain this independence. With this understanding came a flood of investment in the form of European capital. With the abundant foreign capital available, roads, railroads, harbor improvements and canals were possible on a wide scale. Foreign capital also fired the energy of private interests in developing new methods and technologies for freight handling, for developing household and farm machinery and innovative manufacturing techniques of almost every kind. Imaginations raced in expectation of the potential of a mechanized society. Chicago, a tiny village on the outskirts of civilization, was to become the cradle of the industrial age.

The guns of war were scarcely cooled when, in 1816, Major Stephen Long was sent to prepare a comprehensive engineering study of the waterways in the Chicago area, including the prospects for a canal which would complete a continuous waterway from the Great Lakes to the Mississippi River. His report was optimistic and the project was discussed in Congress beginning in 1817. Fort Dearborn was rebuilt, settlers began moving to the area and by 1825 the State had formed a canal company.

11. Lincoln Park Plan
The plan for Lincoln Park was adopted by the City Council, with an appropriation of $10,000 for the first improvements. By 1871, a total of $145,000 had been expended under the supervision of the Board of Public Works. An additional $180,000 had been expended by the Board of Park Commissioners primarily for construction of Lake Shore Drive.

12. Garfield Park, 1910
Horses, bicycles and the newly arrived automobile share the roadway of one of Frederich Law Olmsted's most beautiful parks.

13. Lincoln Park Lagoon, 1870
As the first of a ring of parks around the City, Lincoln Park became a cynosure for residents and tourists. With the development of Calumet Harbor under a federal grant in 1869, the Calumet area 12 miles south of the Chicago area became the center for industrial growth, leaving Chicago's downtown lakefront free for recreational use.

All photographs are on file with the Chicago Historical Society

11

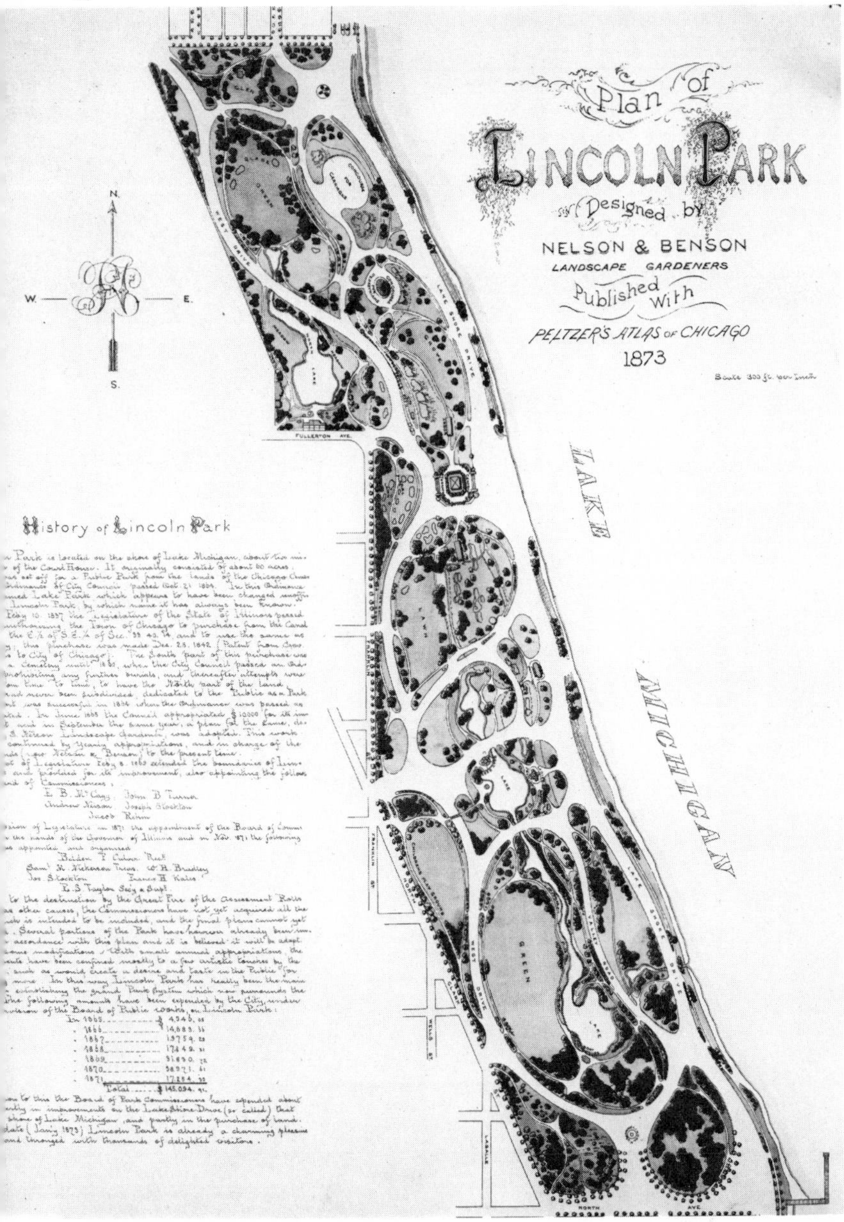
Plan of
Lincoln Park
Designed by
NELSON & BENSON
LANDSCAPE GARDENERS
Published with
PELTZER'S ATLAS OF CHICAGO
1873
N.
W.
E.
S.
FULLERTON AVE.
LAKE
MICHIGAN
NORTH AVE.
History of Lincoln Park

12

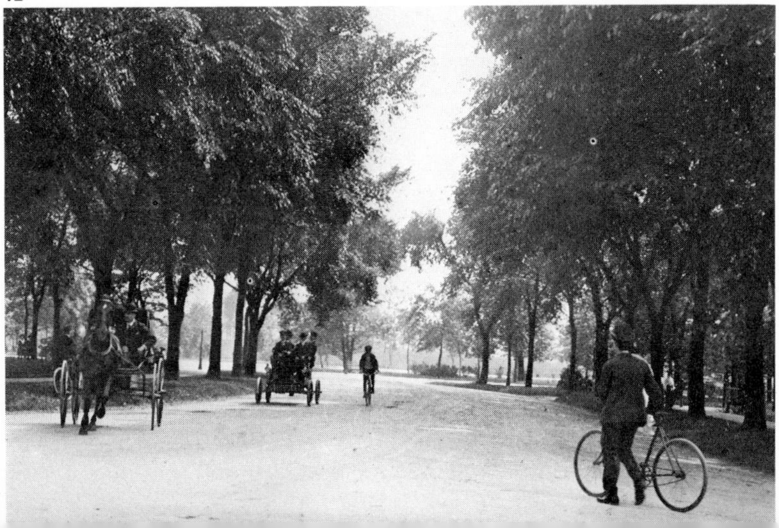

13

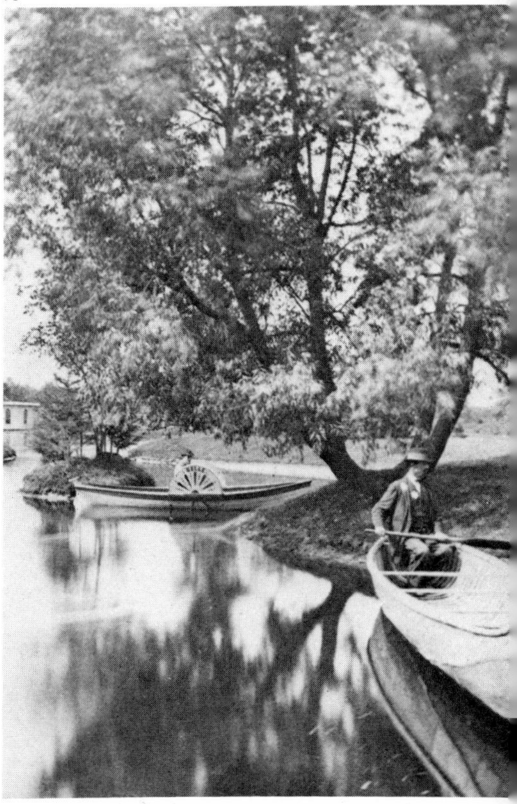

The first exercise of civil authority in the area came in 1823 when Fulton County, which had jurisdiction over the area near Fort Dearborn, imposed a property tax and collected $11.22 on a $2,284 evaluation. In 1830 the state commissioners were authorized to lay out towns along the canal, and a civil engineer, James Thompson, was instructed to survey and plat Chicago. The streets were 66 feet wide, the length of the surveyor's chain consisting of 100 links, laid out in a rectangular grid work. In 1831, Chicago was designated as the seat of justice of the newly formed Cook County. The site for the public buildings, the square block presently occupied by City Hall and the County Building, was selected.

When the Federal government arranged for purchase of all lands east of the Mississippi from the Indians, Chicago emerged from the shadow of Indian deprivations for the first time. The settlement rapidly grew from 60 persons in 1831 to 350 in 1833 when Chicago was organized as a town under State enabling legislation. Fort Dearborn was permanently abandoned by the Army in 1836, and on March 4, 1837, the legislature granted Chicago a city charter.

To the casual observer, it might seem that the driving force which engineering was to become was not yet apparent. The facts are that even the boundaries of the states and the location of Chicago were determined by engineering decisions based on engineering considerations. Nowhere is this more evident than in the selection of the state boundaries for Illinois. Had the original plans been followed, Illinois would have had only four miles of lake front, and what is now Chicago and most of Cook County would have been in Wisconsin. However, the engineering plans for the canal and water route called for the development of the Chicago River rather than the Calumet area. Consequently, an amendment to the original boundary plan was submitted to Congress which included 8,000 square miles of what was to have been southern Wisconsin, on the basis that the canal and associated waterways could be more efficiently administered by one state rather than two. This plan was adopted by Congress and signed into law by President Monroe in 1818. It is interesting to note that the heavy commerce which originated in the main branch of the Chicago River, gradually transferred to the Calumet River in the late 19th century; today most shipping commerce is situated within the boundaries as originally specified. The dominance of canal shipping which played such a dramatic part in the development and organization of Chicago lasted not more than 30 years and was soon replaced by the rapid growth of the railroad, illustrating that the crucial concerns of one era may be of little consequence in another.

Yet a vital principle had been established: engineering decisions could take precedence over other considerations. Stimulation of commerce and development were more important than earlier boundary agreements.

14. Park System, 1871
To provide recreation and relief from the ever increasing densely populated residential neighborhoods, a magnificent park system was developed. Six major park areas were located throughout the city, the parks linked together with broad, landscaped boulevards insuring that each citizen was within one-half hour's distance of a park. The first, Lincoln Park, was built on the lake from land previously set aside for a cemetery. Humboldt, Garfield, Douglas, Jackson and Washington parks followed. By 1870, bicycling, lawn tennis, boating, baseball, riding, dancing, ice skating, and concerts all were available to the public. Arc lamps installed in Lincoln Park became a night time attraction for residents and tourists alike.

15. McKinley Park, 1903
Another example of the large open spaces available in earlier days is shown here. The ornamental light fixture is a direct current, 2400 watt flaming-arc lamp.

16. Jackson Park Ball Game, 1900
The site of the World Columbian Exposition later became a popular park hosting baseball, lawn tennis, boating and picnics; Washington Park offered horse racing as well. Both Jackson and Washington parks were part of the original 1,000 acre South Park.

All photographs are on file with the Chicago Historical Society

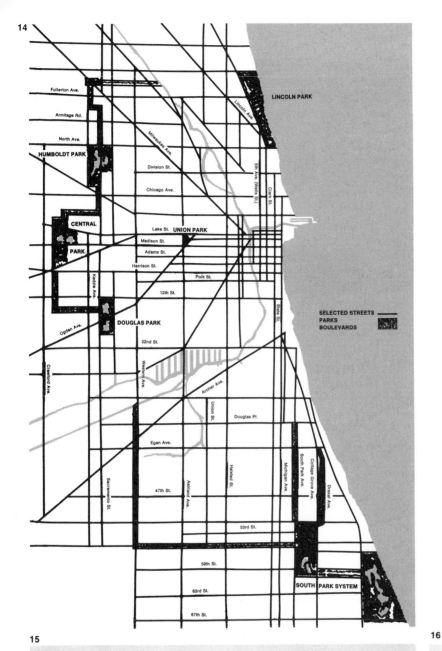

14

Fullerton Ave.

Armitage Rd.

North Ave.

LINCOLN PARK

Milwaukee Ave.

5th Ave. (Wells St.)

Lincoln Ave.

Clark St.

HUMBOLDT PARK

Division St.

Chicago Ave.

CENTRAL

Lake St.   UNION PARK

PARK

Madison St.

Adams St.

Harrison St.

Kedzie Ave.

Polk St.

12th St.

State St.

SELECTED STREETS
PARKS
BOULEVARDS

Ogden Ave.

DOUGLAS PARK

22nd St.

Crawford Ave.

Western Ave.

Archer Ave.

Union St.

Douglas Pl.

Egan Ave.

Sacramento St.

47th St.

Ashland Ave.

Halsted St.

Michigan Ave.

South Park Ave.

Cottage Grove Ave.

Drexel Ave.

53rd St.

59th St.

63rd St.

SOUTH PARK SYSTEM

67th St.

15

16

13

Cradle of Industry

The American Revolution and the Industrial Revolution came at about the same time in history. The nation was then almost wholly agricultural despite the inducements which the Federal government gave to develop manufacturing capability. Well established communities in the original colonies were slow to change their traditional roles and the development of manufacturing fell mainly to the newly emerging cities. Chicago was among these.

Using machines to make machines was one of the new concepts which came about the same time Chicago came into being. Mechanical engineering began to be important about 1820 and became one of the nucleus elements of the growing city.

It was a cyclic process: If machines were made which increased farm production, then other machines and new techniques had to be devised to increase the ability to process and transport these farm products. Soon the processing and sorting techniques themselves captivated the public attention.

With the coming of the shipping canal and the railroads, the growth in trade was enormous. At first the city's paramount position as one of the great markets of the 19th century was associated with the extractive economy of that day; Chicago's trade consisted principally in the assembly and distribution of raw crops, meat packing, flour milling, tanning, lumber and metals. By 1870, it is said the price of the world's bread was decided in Chicago; the Board of Trade remains the greatest speculative grain market in the world today.

Toward the middle of the 19th century, a period of intensive industrialism began. Chicago is still the largest producer of farm machinery in the world and holds the same position in the manufacture of telephone equipment, as well as occupying a prominent position in most fields of manufacturing for wholesale and retail markets in such diverse areas as printing and publishing, chemicals, transportation equipment and electronic equipment, furniture and clothing. Thirty percent of the nation's exports originate from Chicago, testimony to the impact of industrialization.

17. Michigan Avenue Lagoon 1864
An Illinois Central train is visible on the trestle enclosing this waterfront area on Michigan Avenue. Looking north, the giant grain elevators along the river are visible in the background.

18. Illinois-Central Railroad, 1864
In 1848, the year the canal opened, Chicago was without a single mile of track; yet within 6 years, by 1854, Chicago was the rail center of the West. First to the Atlantic, and then to the Pacific, the railroads made Chicago the focus of a growing transcontinental network. Shown here is a wood burning locomotive of the Illinois Central Railroad, looking south along the lake shore. Prior to 1871, the railroad was on a trestle enclosing a lagoon area along Michigan Avenue. This lagoon was filled with debris from the 1871 Fire.

19. Grain Elevators Along the Chicago River
Visitors to Chicago were astonished by the immense size and height of the grain elevators and by the enormous quantities of grain which could be handled rapidly and conveniently using new, innovative techniques. Railway cars entered directly into many of the grain elevators.

20. Lumber Yards, 1871
The largest center for lumber distribution in the world occupied nearly ten miles of river frontage along the South Branch. Illinois and Michigan canal boats are visible in the background. Associated industries included pre-cut houses, planing mills, furniture manufacturing and wagon and ship building.

21. The Wigwam Convention Hall, 1860
Credentials as a convention center were established in 1847 when Chicago, a city of 16,000, played host to 20,000 delegates. In 1860, leading citizens built, within a five week period, the Wigwam to attract the Republican Convention where Abraham Lincoln was nominated. In all, 40 presidential candidates have been nominated in Chicago with 9 elected: Lincoln, Grant, Cleveland, Harrison, Theodore Roosevelt, Taft, Harding, Franklin Roosevelt (twice), and Eisenhower.

14

17

18

20

19

21

The Nail and the Fire

The growth of Chicago was and remains today a unique phenomenon even among U.S. cities. This remarkable growth was related to several factors: the availability of large numbers of Europeans looking for new opportunities, the favorable immigration laws of the time, and the large number of jobs available in Chicago which could be performed even if the individual was not fluent in the language.

Another important factor, however, was the invention of the common household nail. Although nails date to Roman times, these were forged nails, too expensive for housing construction. The so-called mass produced wire nail was not manufactured until the 19th century.

Until this time, the practical method of house construction which had remained unchanged for hundreds—even thousands—of years was that of mortising and tenoning joints of heavy timber which were then pegged together. With the availability of the nail, a radical new construction method called balloon construction developed in the mid-19th century: Light-weight, two-by-four studs were nailed together in a basket-like arrangement from the foundation. Uninjured by mortise and tenon, with every strain coming in the direction of the wood fibre, the fragile looking skeleton was actually exceptionally strong. Historians agree that without this time and labor-saving method of construction, the mushrooming cities of the American West could never have been built as quickly as they were: San Francisco and Chicago are striking examples.

Consequently, fire was always a continual threat to cities put together with lumber; two-thirds of Chicago buildings were only of wood, as were most sidewalks and fences. Many cities, Chicago among them, suffered a number of conflagrations during the 19th century; but no city ever endured the holocaust that nearly destroyed Chicago in the Great Fire of 1871.

The fire began near the lumber district on the west side, said according to legend to be on the O'Leary property. Chicago had suffered 27 major fires during the first week of October, one major blaze just the day before. Fanned by a

22. O'Leary Residence, 1871
At DeKoven Street, where the Great Fire was believed to have begun, the wooden O'Leary house stimulated much interest in the period following the fire. Today it is the site of the new Fire Academy, after being named a historical site in 1937. The O'Leary house, a structure held together only with nails, is an example of balloon frame construction, a technique developed in Chicago by Augustine Taylor and first used in the building of St. Mary's Church near the corner of State and Lake streets in 1833.

23. Map of Area Destroyed by the Great Fire of 1871
One of the most spectacular events of the civilized world, the Chicago Fire of 1871 became a convenient yardstick to measure other disasters. No photographs of the Fire survived.

24. Courthouse Ruins, 1871
The magnitude of the catastrophe is visible in this photograph of the central business area showing the complete devastation with only the walls of the courthouse standing.

All photographs are on file with the Chicago Historical Society

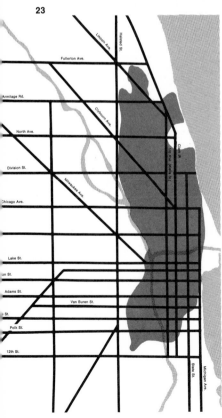

23

24

strong wind and feeding on the combustible materials of the lumber mills, within two hours a sheet of flame a hundred feet high roared toward downtown Chicago. By morning, most of the city was gone: fireproof structures and shanties alike, the bridges, ships at anchor, and the railroad yards; All public works systems were in ruins and 100,000 people were homeless.

25

26

27

25, 26. The Illinois Central Terminal, 1860 and 1871
This busy terminal was completely destroyed in the Fire of 1871, as shown in the before and after pictures.

27. Hotel Skeleton
The Tremont, one of the city's first fashionable hotels at Lake and Dearborn, was demolished. The Tremont was designed by John Van Osdel, a Chicago architect famous for the design of grain elevators. This hotel was one of those raised by jacks to meet the new grade in 1867.

28. State Street, 1871
What had been one of the great mercantile boulevards of the nineteenth century became an impassable shambles of bent street car rails with tangled skeins of telegraph wire, while the shell of a limestone church waits the hammer of demolition. The so-called spotted limestone of which most churches were made contained blotches of petroleum which were said to have helped spread the flames. This rumor was disproved when a study showed that the spotted limestone withstood the fire better than the Athens marble which exploded with the intense heat.

29. Post Office Remains
According to legend, "neither snow nor rain nor sleet nor gloom of night" could halt mail delivery. The Great Fire left the walls from the post office standing but little else. 15,000 water service pipes actually melted in the intense heat.

30. Water Tower and Pumping Station
The walls of the Waterworks were of stone with a slate-covered roof; the structure was isolated in the middle of a block with streets on three sides and the lake at the rear. A 12 foot piece of burning debris, blown by the high wind punctured the roof igniting the interior woodwork and floors, gutting the interior and cutting off the city's water supply.

All photographs are on file with the Chicago Historical Society

28

29

30

A Phoenix Ascends

The fire that destroyed the residential and business areas left most of the industrial establishments untouched. The work force was still intact and the economic posture of the nation was strong.

Reconstruction began as fast as the rubble could be cleared. The debris was used as lake fill around the Illinois Central tracks and added land to the public domain valued at the rate of $1,000 per day; this "made land," a hundred years later was to be called "the most valuable real estate in the world."

Within a year after the Fire, the Board of Public Works issued 1,250 building permits for 965 brick, 200 stone, 65 frame, and 20 iron structures; among them was a temporary court house. The City also replaced 72 miles of wooden sidewalks and street pavement. The greatest municipal expenditure, however, involved repairing the water system at a cost of $248,410 and beginning construction of another water tunnel of much larger capacity than the original one built to serve the first two mile intake crib.

Twelve months after the fire the business district was largely rebuilt of stone and brick structures since the Council had passed an ordinance prohibiting wood structures in the central area. The new business center was more elaborate, ornamental and substantially higher; its five, six, and seven story buildings foreshadowing the birth of the "skyscraper." Thus the city was once more literally elevated, and like the Phoenix, the mythological bird which burned itself and was reborn, Chicago rose from its own ashes to establish a new and greater city.

The post-fire reconstruction attracted architects and builders of rare vision and ability. Richardson, Sullivan, Root, Adler, Burnham, and, later, Wright contributed in distinctive ways to create not only a Chicago School, but a dynamic approach which became national in scope, revolutionizing the building arts.

31. View from Water Tower, 1874
Churches and substantial, multi-story frame buildings characterized the North Side skyline replacing the earlier flimsy cottages, while brick structures made up most of the downtown area.

32. Rebuilding the Central Business District, 1872
During most of 1872, buildings were completed at the rate of one per hour and within three years following the fire, busy thoroughfares lined with tall, marble buildings had replaced the heap of charred ruins. Most new structures were five stories high and some nine, the higher skyline now practical with use of the newly developed elevators. Night time construction went on under illumination from electric lights and in some cases, as at the Palmer House, under vapor arc lamps. By mixing salt with mortar, bricklaying continued through the winter. Shown is the Marine Building, which stood until 1928 at the northeast corner of Lake and LaSalle, rebuilt to six stories and later to seven stories, replacing a pre-fire four story building. Derrick hoists, visible in this photograph, represented a new innovation in construction; this design principle was later incorporated in modern elevator design.

All photographs are on file with the Chicago Historical Society

32

The Chicago Plan

The 1893 World's Columbian Exposition marked the 400th anniversary of the landing of Christopher Columbus in the New World. In Jackson Park, bordering on Lake Michigan, a "City Beautiful" of ancient Greek and Roman grandeur was constructed, graced by landscaped reflecting pools and fountains, and by lagoons with Venetian gondolas. Although architects objected to the lack of originality in building design and complained that the cultural level of the populace was not raised by exposure to scaled copies of ancient facades and sculpture, the fair nevertheless illustrated a new concept: creating beauty, order and harmony through an inter-relationship of buildings, and open space, in a planned city.

The fair became the chief inspiration for the plan for Chicago. In 1907, the Commercial Club of Chicago asked a leading architect, Daniel Hudson Burnham, to prepare a comprehensive plan for Chicago. The plan was presented to the City as a gift, with the Club financing the effort for several years until the City assumed responsibility.

Burnham saw Chicago primarily as an industrial city and his plan was designed to free industry and commerce from the strangling effects of congestion while at the same time insuring Chicagoans of an agreeable place to work and live which would be aesthetically pleasing as well as practical and convenient.

The natural configuration and beauty of the river and lakefront together with stately vistas and settings for public buildings form the central theme of Burnham's plan. A proposed expressway system included a series of diagonal highways leading from the civic center to the outer borders of the city, with concentric rings of outer drives at convenient distances. The plan specified in detail a great variety of public buildings, a magnificent park system together with various river and lakefront improvements, producing a quality of symmetry and elegance.

Many of Burnham's proposed projects have long since been completed and still others are presently in the construction stage. The outer ring of parks and forest preserves, the public

33. **World's Columbian Exposition, 1893–1894**
Celebrating four centuries of progress since the discovery of America, the World's Fair was a planned and orderly city, integrating the beauty of gardens, waterways and structures in contrast to the chaotic disorder of most of America's fast growing cities. The exposition came to be known as The White City and served as a chief source of inspiration for modern city planning. The Fine Arts Building survives today as The Museum of Science and Industry in Jackson Park. The Midway Plaisance near today's University of Chicago was the site of the circus rides; the carnival term "midway" was coined from the Fair. Twenty four banks closed in 1893, the most severe depression of the 19th Century, and unemployed soared, but the Fair with 21 million paid admissions was a great success.

34. **Chicago Plan, 1909**
Highly symmetrical in design, the original Plan provided a complete system of traffic circulation, together with an integrated plan for open spaces and civic buildings. Navy Pier was built just south of the location shown here at Chicago Avenue.

35. **Proposed Wacker Drive**
This sketch shows the original plan to separate riverfront activity from the city traffic by raising the boulevards.

All photographs are on file with the Chicago Historical Society

buildings and widened thoroughfares, Field Museum, Shedd
Aquarium, Adler Planetarium, Navy Pier, the Chicago
Historical Society Building in Lincoln Park, Museum of
Science and Industry, the cultural complex comprising the
Public Library, the Art Center, Orchestra Hall, Fine Arts
Building, the Auditorium and Soldier Field are all derived from
this plan which became a bastion of strength and guidance to
future generations of planning commissions. Chicago
continued to foster the growth of urban planning techniques
over the years and today commands a preeminent position in
its important field.

35

33

34

Into The Twentieth Century

When Mark Twain first saw Berlin in the early 1920's, he called this stately, industrial city, *"The Chicago of Germany."* As Twain observed, great cities have special visual qualities. Land formations and waterways may form recognizable and coherent patterns; certain landmarks may be easily identifiable. Chicago, a tall, stately city rising out of the vast prairie beside the lake possessed this striking image since the turn of the century.

The world's first skyscrapers were built in Chicago before 1900. Even though these buildings would look small today, the pattern of vertical expansion has helped maintain a viable downtown business district, the same business district since the formation of the city.

The advent of the modern technological society brought significant changes to the urban scene. Just as Chicago was once the busiest rail center in the world, today O'Hare Airport is the busiest airport in the world. The facilities change but the concentration in transportation remains. To a large degree, the essential character of the city remains unchanged in this century. The grain exchange still dominates Midwest financial affairs. Trade of all kinds remains an essential part of the economic life. Manufacturing and industrial activities have changed in product but still remain highly diversified. Today, as in the early days, the production of iron, steel, lumber, agricultural equipment, clothing, furniture, meat packing, food processing, chemicals and paints, household industries, retail merchandise, printing and publishing are still prominent throughout the city. When, in 1959, the St. Lawrence Seaway was completed and Chicago became a world port, shipping once again increased, revitalizing the in-land waterway traffic reminiscent of early days in the city's life, now incorporating overseas commerce.

Throughout this period of expansion and growth, all the problems which beset major urban centers developed in Chicago. To combat urban blight and deterioration, and to stimulate new growth and development, a wide variety of public work programs have been created to improve the quality of life in Chicago. This is the story of those public works.

36. Century of Progress, 1933
Chicago's second world's fair brought bright lights and encouragement to a nation in the grips of the Great Depression. Despite the hard times, the fair was a financial success, providing much needed employment and lifting of spirits for some forty million people who attended. The popular Skyride, seen in this photograph, crossing the Northerly Island Lagoon, was the tallest structure in Chicago, taking its riders 628 feet in the air. It was higher than any other non-building in the nation, topping the Washington Monument at 555 feet.

37. High Rise Skylines
Chicago was the breeding ground for the world's first skyscrapers built in the late 19th century. The development of the cast iron column and beam sections used as frames led to the steel beam column construction which formed the basic structural frame used until after World War II. Within the last decade, engineers have achieved maximum strength and stiffness by connecting all columns, creating a hollow tube punctured with windows. A 100 story building, with tubular design, will use no more steel than a 35 story building built by conventional design, with up to 150 stories possible without design modification. The Hancock Building, Sears Tower, Standard Oil Building and the New York Trade Center are examples of tubular construction.

38. Chicago Skyline, 1950
Chicago rising beside the lake has always been a striking sight since the turn of the century, even at a time as shown here when the buildings were not as tall as today. Until the 42 story Prudential Building was built in 1955, no major buildings had been constructed in the Loop since the early 1930's.

39. Chicago Skyline, 1973
The rapidly changing skyline creates problems for tourist guide books and magazines which must be revised annually. From 1966–1971, total construction exceeded $7.8 billion in Chicago. This figure was the largest for any metropolitan area in the country. Further, Chicago led in every construction category: industrial, commercial and residential.

36

38

39

37

Prudential Bldg.	Lake Point Tower	Civic Center	IBM Bldg.	First Nat'l. Bank	John Hancock Center	Standard Oil Bldg.	Empire State Bldg.	World Trade Center	Sears Tower
1954	1967	1965	1971	1968	1968	1973 (Est.)	1931	1973 (Est.)	1974 (Est.)
601 Ft.	645 Ft.	662 Ft.	695 Ft.	850 Ft.	1107 Ft.	1136 Ft.	New York City	New York City	1450 Ft.
							1250 Ft.	1350 Ft.	

Great Pyramid of Cheops	Pharos Lighthouse	Eiffel Tower	Monadnock Bldg.	Wrigley Bldg.	Tribune Tower	Playboy Bldg.	Marina City
3000 B. C.	280 B. C.	1889	1891	1924	1925	1929	1964
Giza, Egypt	Alexandria, Egypt	Paris	215 Ft.	398 Ft.	462 Ft.	468 Ft.	588 Ft.
481 Ft.	600 Ft. (Est.)	942 Ft.					

10-10-04

Rivers and Canals   2

**Construction of the Chicago
Sanitary and Ship Canal, 1894**
*One of the wonders of the world, and
requiring more earth moving than the
construction of the Panama Canal,
the Chicago Sanitary and Ship Canal
succeeded in reversing the flow of the
Chicago River. For the first time in more
than 10,000 years, the Great Lakes area
drained into the Gulf of Mexico as the only
watershed other than that of the St.
Lawrence River draining to the Atlantic.
The scope of this engineering feat is
particularly impressive when the primitive
equipment of the last century is
considered, as shown in this photograph
taken midway through construction on
October 10, 1894.*

First Harbor Installations

A troublesome sand bar hampered entry into the Chicago River. Although shallow draft ships could enter the port, larger cargo vessels were forced to anchor off shore and transfer their cargo to small boats for passage through shallow waters near the river mouth.

In 1830, the Federal government began construction of a harbor by digging a channel through the sandbar, called "the deep cut" in contrast to the earlier shallow cut made by the soldiers at Fort Dearborn in 1818. The cut was finished in 1833 at a cost of $25,000; the chief engineer was Jefferson Davis, later to be known as President of the Confederacy during the Civil War.

Suddenly, Chicago became the leading port in the West. A pier 1,000 feet long was built along the north shore of the river through the sandbar. Additional Federal funds were solicited for further harbor improvements, and by autumn of 1835, the north pier had been extended 1260 feet and the south pier 700 feet into the lake with a channel 200 feet wide at depths of from three to seven feet. This still was not sufficient, so a dredge boat was provided by the Corps of Engineers to deepen the channel sufficiently to accommodate the largest lake boats. After achieving this short-sighted objective, the dredge boat was towed away to another port.

By 1838, Congress had appropriated almost $200,000 for harbor improvements, but each extension of the pier resulted in another sandbar at the new end. Thus, the shore lines progressively moved east, about 720 feet along the north pier between 1833 and 1839. Probably the best brief summation of all these efforts is in the words of Andreas, noted Chicago historian, who observed: *"one continued series of experiments."* In 1839, with the channel again filling, ships drawing more than eight feet of water precariously entered the harbor but only with great difficulty.

Obviously, a new plan was needed because the city's prosperity depended on its harbor. A number of meetings were held to discuss possible solutions. Further dredging was decided upon and through private subscription, funds were raised to bring the dredge boat back to Chicago.

In the meantime, a memorandum addressed to Congress in 1841 from Chicago set forth the deplorable condition of the harbor and requested *"immediate permanent"* relief, warning that if assistance should not be granted soon, *"commerce would be without shelter and human life and property endangered to a lamentable extent."* Chicago's claims were vigorously pressed in Congress and in 1843 and 1844, two appropriations totaling $55,000 were granted to the City. These sums were used for the extension and elevation of the north pier to a length of almost 3,000 feet.

This improvement together with dredging created a more commodious channel. Seeing no further need for the dredging barge, the City allowed it to be towed away again, and this time it was sunk. By the spring of 1847, however, another sandbar began to obstruct the harbor entrance. Thus, after almost $250,000 had been expended on the harbor at Chicago, the situation was once more critical. That year, the steamer *Genessee Chief* ran aground and once again the larger ships were compelled to anchor outside the harbor and transfer their cargos by lighters.

Again aroused, the City Council authorized a four-year loan of $1000 to meet the expense of raising the sunken dredge, repairing it, and returning it to Chicago to clear the harbor, but this was never done.

After the $55,000 in appropriations by Congress in 1843 and 1844, no further Federal funds were forthcoming until 1852, when Congress granted $20,000 for inner harbor improvements. The principal shipping hazard was a persistent submerged sandbar formed by currents swirling around the end of the north pier. The bar extended in a southeasterly direction, forcing ships to approach from the south, then turn abruptly west to enter the river. Each time a channel was dredged through the sandbar it quickly refilled with the first northerly winds.

Channel dredging was continued by the City in 1863 and '64, and in 1865 the pier was extended 510 feet farther east, but this served simply to transfer the sandbar problem to the new location. Pier construction at that time consisted of wood cribs built in sections up to 400 feet long, 24 feet wide and 21 feet high. The cribs were floated to the site, filled with stone and sunk to the pre-dredged level bottom so that the top extended about six feet above normal water level.

The persistent sandbar problem was not solved until the federal government again extended the north pier in 1867, this time in connection with construction of an outer harbor breakwater. Finally, in 1869, Washington recognized that the Chicago Harbor was a national asset and took over complete responsibility for preserving the entrance.

The Illinois and Michigan Canal

Early explorers and voyageurs to the Chicago Portage saw the potential of a short canal through marshy Mud Lake. In 1673, French explorer Louis Joliet wrote in his report:
"It would only be necessary to make a canal, by cutting through but half a league of prairie, to pass from the foot of the lake to the river which falls into the Mississippi. The bark, when there, would sail easily into the Gulf of Mexico."

A less enthusiastic view was expressed by another French explorer, LaSalle, who in 1682 wrote, that the canal was *"proposed without regard to its difficulties."*

The practicability and need for a canal connecting the Illinois River with Lake Michigan was recognized and discussed for many years. A French military engineer named Victor Collot, as a result of explorations made in 1790, pointed out that it was highly probable that "the lakes Michigan and Superior emptied their waters formerly into this river (Mississippi);" for he noted that when the waters were high, *"boats carrying from 15 to 20 thousand weight"* passed from the Illinois River to Lake Michigan without a portage by traversing a marsh which joined the sources of the Illinois River with those of the Chicago River. In 1807, Secretary of the Treasury Alvert Gallatin made a similar report to Congress, except that he called Mud Lake a *"swamp."*

In 1816, Major Stephen Long was sent to examine the portages of the Fox and Wisconsin rivers and headwaters of the Mississippi River. His report was the first comprehensive engineering feasibility and planning study for a proposed canal. It concluded that the most suitable site for a canal would be in the Chicago portage area connecting the Illinois and the Chicago rivers. The report concluded that construction would be a simple and inexpensive matter.

The project was discussed in Congress in 1817 and 1818. Then in 1819 the Secretary of War, Henry Calhoun, reported that such a canal would be essential to carry on military

1, 2. 19th Century Construction of the I & M Canal
Three cannon sounded at Fort Dearborn and citizens assembled in the public square, moved in a body to the construction site on July 4, 1836, for inauguration ceremonies. Under Chief Engineer William Gooding, the work proceeded slowly owing to scarcity of labor and sickness, and was not completed until 12 years after initiation. While continual flooding and heavy rain had hindered construction, the operation of the canal was hampered by a shortage of water and unusually low waters in the Illinois River. In June, 1856, navigation of the river was suspended for six months. In the first decade of operation, over $1 million in tolls were collected chiefly from lumber, pork, grain and coal. The largest annual toll collected was over $300,000 in 1866. Today coal, oil and cement are the principal cargos shipped along Chicago's inland waterways.

1. Construction Photograph, mid-1800s
Original Title—"Drainage Channel and Waterway in Rock. Full width and One-Third Required Depth".

2. Construction Photograph, mid-1800s
Original Title—"Rock in Drainage Channel and Waterway after Blasting". The photographs in this section were taken from Drainage Channel and Waterway, by G.P. Brown, R.R. Donnelley & Sons, Chicago, 1894.

All photographs are on file with the Chicago Historical Society

operations in time of war "for the defense of the western portion of our Northern frontier."

In June, 1823, Major Long, while his expedition was on the way to explore the source of the St. Peter's River in Minnesota, again visited various possible localities for the proposed canal.

"We are irresistibly led to the conclusion that an elevation of the lakes of a few feet above their present level would cause them to discharge their water into the Gulf of Mexico; such discharge has at one time existed; and it is equally apparent that an expenditure, trifling in comparison with the importance of the object, would again render Lake Michigan a tributary of the Mexican Gulf."

In the autumn of 1823, Colonel Justus Post, appointed chief engineer, made a tour of exploration along the proposed canal route, but nothing definite was accomplished. The next year Colonel Post and Rene Paul of St. Louis, an able engineer, each accompanied by a crew, started at opposite ends and met in the middle to complete the survey. Five different routes were surveyed, and cost estimates were made on each. In January, 1825, the commissioners made their report to the legislature, sending also a copy to President Adams, for consideration as a possible Federal project. A few days later, on January 17, the State Legislature passed an act to incorporate the *"Illinois and Michigan Canal Company."*

Work on the canal did not begin until the Fourth of July, 1836. Unfortunately, the soft clay surface disguised the limestone bedrock underneath. By 1841, funds had run out with the canal only partly completed. Although a number of contractors were ruined and the population dwindled with the slumping economy, the fervor of that auspicious beginning did not diminish during the lean years between 1838 and 1843, when the state found itself in possession of a partially completed canal and burdened with a debt of almost $4.8 million. To Chicago, the I & M Canal still represented the bright light of hope for the future.

Realizing that it probably would be impossible to raise another $3 million to complete the deep cut, which would once more, after 10,000 years, make Lake Michigan a tributary of the Mississippi, supporters of the project fell back on a "shallow cut" alternative scheme. This would involve feeding the I & M with water from the DesPlaines and Calumet rivers and would require much less excavation. It was estimated that the canal could thus be finished at an additional cost of only $1.6 million.

The legislature delayed making a decision for there was still doubt whether sufficient water could be obtained from the feeders to operate the canal on the high level of the shallow-cut. This was resolved by a plan to raise the level of the canal by installing immense steam pumps in Bridgeport and pumping water from the South Branch to the summit

3. Construction Photograph, mid-1800s
Original Title—"Excavation in Earth for Drainage Channel and Waterway. One Third Depth."

4. Construction Photograph, late 1870s
Original Title—"New Channel for Diversion of the Desplaines River."

All photographs are on file with the Chicago Historical Society

3

4

above the DesPlaines River. The legislature subsequently approved completion of the canal following this shallow-cut plan.

Operations for completing the canal commenced in July, 1845, despite a shortage of labor, rampant sickness among the workers in the valley of the Illinois in 1846, and a strike in 1847.

By April, 1848, all was ready for the passage of the first boat, and on the 10th, the *General Fry* passed over the summit at Chicago with the formal opening on April 16, 1848. The keynote speaker said: *"The completion of the Canal, connecting the Lakes with the navigable waters of the Mississippi, will at once, and by magic, change the condition and prospects of our City; increase its population; introduce capital to operate in our staples, produce, provisions, lumber; enlarge every avenue of commerce, and promote the growth of manufactures. The arteries of trade will be opened, and commerce will flow freely through them."*

5. Construction Photograph, mid-1800s
Original Title—"Excavation in Rock for Drainage Channel and Waterway. Full Depth in Center."

All photographs are on file with the Chicago Historical Society

5

Chicago Sanitary and Ship Canal

The enormous expansion of the city by 1850, the growth of commerce and industry, and the increasing population created a menace to health as a result of lake pollution by domestic sewage and industrial wastes. Typhoid fever, amoebic dysentery, and cholera were sometimes rampant scourges.

As early as 1864, deepening the Illinois and Michigan Canal was proposed so as to cause a gravity flow from the lake towards the DesPlaines River. The project was subsequently undertaken and the deep cut was completed in 1871 at a cost of three million dollars.

The result was disappointing because the changing water levels of the river and the lake made the scheme unreliable. Furthermore, during the spring, flood waters rushed toward Lake Michigan; when the lake was at high water, the city was relieved but only to add to the distress of communities downstream on the DesPlaines and Illinois rivers.

Another attempt at flushing the river away from the lake was made in 1876, when the Fullerton Avenue Conduit and Pumping Stations were built. This also proved to be unsatisfactory, and still another attempt to control the reversed flow of the river was initiated in 1884 with the installation of water pumps in Bridgeport at the junction of the canal and the South Branch. This system worked for a year; however, it was overburdened when the Ogden-Wentworth ditch was cut into the west fork of the South Branch to drain Mud Lake.

The final blow came the following year. On August 2 and 3, 1885, a total of 6.19 inches of rain fell in and around the city. The subsequent flood waters completely overwhelmed the giant pumps and sent the scourings of sewers and catch basins into the river and then into the lake where they formed an immense foul mass of wastes teeming with virulent bacteria. There was an immediate and alarming rise in the disease death rate from water-borne diseases.

In January, 1886, the City Council authorized the appointment of a Drainage and Water Supply Commission to work out an ultimate solution to the whole sanitary and water supply situation of Chicago.

6. Chicago Sanitary and Ship Canal
Title of photograph: "Junction of Earth and Rock Sections at Willow Springs, Illinois." The photographs shown here were taken from a report, The Chicago Drainage Channel, by the Special Commission, to the Governor of Illinois, 1900.
The reversing of the river flow was named one of the "seven modern civil engineering wonders" in the United States by the American Society of Civil Engineers in 1954. The other six awards named were the Panama Canal, Empire State Building, Colorado River Aqueduct, Grand Coulee Dam, Hoover Dam and San Francisco Bay Bridge.

All photographs are on file with the Chicago Historical Society

6

In 1892, the City embarked on the largest single earth moving project in the history of the municipal public works: the Sanitary and Ship Canal, a 28-mile cut through the glacial moraine and bedrock ridge west of Chicago, not only to create a continuous navigable waterway between the Great Lakes and the interior rivers but once more, after 10,000 years, to make Lake Michigan a tributary to the Mississippi River. While the I & M Canal was a geographic modification which created a continuous waterway, the Sanitary and Ship Canal was to completely reverse the flow of the Chicago River in order to prevent contamination of the city's water supply and to dispose of its domestic and industrial wastes. The canal was planned to connect the South Branch of the Chicago River, at now Damen Avenue, to the DesPlaines River at Lockport.

As nearly half of the planned route occupied the bed of the DesPlaines River, it was necessary to dig a 13-mile channel to divert the river. With the river rerouted, the canal was excavated through 15 miles of solid rock, 7.8 miles of earth, and 5.3 miles of combined earth and rock as a force of 8,500 men swung into action for eight years. By 1900, 29,559,000 cubic yards of earth were removed and 12,261,000 cubic yards of rock were blasted and hauled away. This channel terminated in a control structure consisting of sluice gates and Bear Trap Dam which provided the means for regulating the amount of water to flow through the canal.

Work was completed January 2, 1900 and on the 17th the gates were opened. Great crowds of people once more gathered on the banks of the river in Chicago, this time to see whether the river would actually flow "backward," as the engineers predicted. It did—the river was reversed—and since that day the Chicago River has steadily flowed from Lake Michigan.

A city newspaper named *Inter Ocean* claimed the project was *"the greatest and most important municipal undertaking in modern time."*

During the three decades preceding the opening of the drainage canal the average death rate from typhoid fever in Chicago was 65 persons per 100,000. The rate was halved a decade after the Chicago River was reversed and by 1922, when the drainage system was completed, the typhoid death rate had dropped to one per 100,000 residents. In addition to protecting the municipal water supply, the drainage gave still another benefit —the finest lake front of any city in the world.

Although the reversal of the Chicago River solved the problem for Chicago, neighboring states on the Great Lakes protested that Chicago was draining the lake and sued the Drainage District to prevent it from taking water out of Lake Michigan. As a result of this law suit, the diversion was reduced from 10,000 to 3,000 cubic feet per second and controlling locks placed at the river inlet.

7. Lockport, 1900
The Metropolitan Sanitary District opened the Bear Trap flood gates at Lockport on January 17, 1900, marking the completion of the canal.

8. General Plan of the Chicago Drainage Canal
Completed in less than a decade, the construction of the canal was one of the greatest engineering achievements of all time, requiring more land excavation than the construction of the Panama Canal. When completed, the waters of Lake Michigan began draining to the Gulf of Mexico, and the Chicago River became the only river in the world to run backwards.

9. Construction Photograph, July 10, 1894
Mule drawn graders did the work of the greatest earth moving operation of the century.

All photographs are on file with the Chicago Historical Society

7

8

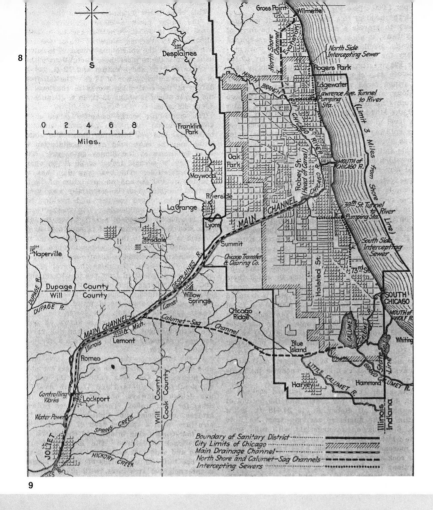

99-D 7-10 94

Calumet Harbor

The concept of the Industrial Park was introduced in Chicago about 1893, the time of the annexation of the Calumet Harbor area and surroundings, 12 miles south of downtown Chicago. The objective of the Industrial Park was to bring together compatible business and industries and by working together with urban planners, create a viable industrial complex including streets, utilities and other needed services to encourage industrial development.

Calumet was ideal for such industrial expansion since the area had a natural harbor, a large lake region inland and extensive open and as yet undeveloped land areas. The Federal government had provided grants for improving the harbor as early as 1869, and with cargo ships using the harbor beginning in 1871.

Heavy industry quickly moved into the area. The six miles along the Calumet River between Lake Michigan and Lake Calumet concentrated the industrial might of the Midwest, rivaling any industrial complex in the world. The City moved to provide the basic services and facilities needed by industry and the growing residential community alike.

With the huge blast furnaces of the steel mills and the smoke stacks of the chemical, lumber and other major industries concentrating in the southern Calumet area, heavy commercial traffic gradually declined at the Chicago River.

When Chicago became a world port in 1959 with the opening to the St. Lawrence Seaway, Calumet Harbor was modified to accommodate the ocean-going vessels. Today freighters from over 50 different international lines, flying foreign flags, regularly appear in these harbor facilities and depart for foreign ports. Chicagoans can travel by boat not only to the Gulf of Mexico and onward to South America but can venture overseas to Europe and Africa directly from the Port of Chicago.

10. Lake Calumet, 1870
Activity was just beginning in the Calumet area in 1870. This view is from the old Calumet lighthouse looking west at 92nd Street. The heavy industries of the late 19th Century found an ideal location in Calumet. Here was an inland lake, extensive water supplies for factory operation, an excellent harbor for shipping and close proximity to the railroads, all with vast, unsettled land areas. Within five years of this picture, the dark smoke of the blast furnaces and rolling mills dominated the area, and by 1915, the Calumet area contained the world's greatest concentration of heavy industry.

11. Calumet River Entrance, January, 1973
Winter shrouds the entrance to Chicago's great industrial complex. The first bridge across the river from Lake Michigan is a privately owned railroad swing bridge. The bridge at the river bend is the 92nd Street bascule and in the lower right hand corner is the 95th Street bascule bridge built in 1957. Once industrial developers viewed industrial smoke as symbolic of rising power and affluence. Today all major industries are working to reduce air and water pollution, the latter particularly important at the cul-de-sac end of Lake Michigan near the Calumet Harbor. The United States Steel Company's 600 acre property dominates the photograph in the upper portion; this plant has invested $50 million in programs which include replacing of older open hearths with a basic oxygen process eliminating stack emission; the plant is installing a complete water recycling system which, when placed in operation in 1975, will eliminate discharge of all contaminants from this plant into Lake Michigan. This effort is typical of the joint efforts of industry and government to preserve the environment.

12. Transoceanic Terminal
Located 700 miles from the ocean, the Calumet Harbor services ocean-going vessels such as those shown here. Since 1959 when Chicago became a world port, over $300 million have been invested for port and waterway improvements.

11 12

Navy Pier

The original Chicago Plan called for two piers into the lake on each side of the rivers entrance. Between 1914 and 1916 only one of the twin piers was completed. Called the Municipal Pier and later Navy Pier, it was built at a construction cost of $4,192,310.09.

The pier reached 3000 feet into the water and contained not only docking installations and its own streetcar line, but served as a dance hall, theatre, restaurant and recreational facilities. In the summer, small excursion boats operated from the Pier to Lincoln and Jackson Parks.

During World War II, the Pier was modified for use as a naval training base. Following the War, it was used as University of Illinois at Chicago for thousands of veterans under the G.I. Bill. It was retained as a branch of the University of Illinois until the Circle Campus on Chicago's West Side was opened. Further modifications took place in 1958 in preparations for the first ocean-going vessels coming to port after the opening of the enlarged St. Lawrence Seaway. The Pier was widened by 96 feet along a distance of 1100 feet. Existing cargo sheds were rehabilitated and a new shed constructed. The harbor was dredged from 21 to 29 feet, equal to that of the St. Lawrence Seaway to accommodate international shipping. The *Prins Johan Willem Friso* of the Dutch Orange Line was the first arrival in April, 1959, marking Chicago's entrance as a world port.

13. Navy Pier, 1921
Public transportation served the Pier on tracks located between the sheds. In 1921, public transportation served most of the population. Until 1926, mass transit ridership increased in direct proportion with the population increase, and less than one person in ten owned a car.

14. Navy Pier, June, 1955
From the top of the Sheraton Hotel, looking east at Navy Pier before the Central Water Filtration Plant was constructed at the upper left.

15. Navy Pier, 1916
A center for recreation in the summer, Chicagoans enjoyed themselves by taking excursion boats to Lincoln and Jackson Parks and in the theaters, dancing halls and restuarants at the Pier.

16. Navy Pier, 1959
Chicago became a world port on April 30th, 1959, when the Dutch freighter Prins Johan Willem Friso tied up at Navy Pier after a trip through the St. Lawrence Seaway. A portion of the crowd attending the opening ceremonies are shown here. Although the pier is still used for some commercial exhibitions, shipping is the main activity with an average of 80 overseas ships arriving each year with imports of over 130,000 tons.

17. Navy Pier 1973
With the water filtration plant in the background, and the 70-story Lake Point Tower apartment building on the left, ocean going ships can be seen during the summer months at the Pier.

All photographs are on file with the Chicago Historical Society

13

14

15

16

17

Straightening of the River

Over the years, the Chicago River has endured many cuts and alterations to both straighten and deepen this once narrow, meandering stream, and a host of plans have been studied for improving river passage. The most comprehensive of these was to by-pass the main branch altogether with a new cut directly from the canal to the lake. A less sweeping but practical plan in terms of reduced cost was implemented in the 1920s.

The Chicago River had an awkward bend on the South Branch which impeded shipping traffic and partly isolated the main business district from the South Side. Only three main traffic arteries connected to the south from the Loop: Michigan Avenue, State and Wabash streets.

The coming of the automobile emphasized the need for straightening of the river between Polk and Eighteenth Street. In its essential features, it included removing the bend which blocked the southward extension of LaSalle, Wells and Franklin streets. This required digging a new channel for the river, filling in the old channel, extending the streets and building new bridges over the new channel. These extensions relieved traffic congestion by opening three wide streets from the south side of the Loop so that some of the vehicular load could be removed from narrow Wentworth Avenue, Canal Street and Michigan Avenue on the east.

Using the advanced earth moving techniques developed earlier in Chicago on such massive projects as the Sanitary and Shipping Canal construction, a straight cut was made through what had been primarily vacant land. When the new cut was ready for use, the former river bed was filled in, providing the needed land area so that the main traffic arteries from the Loop could be extended southward.

The new channel was opened to shipping in 1933.

18. Construction of River Straightening, 1926

The meandering river prevented the natural extension of streets from the Loop to the South Side and caused heavy congestion on streets immediately to the east of the river.

All photographs are on file with the Chicago Historical Society

18

The Moving Shoreline

Chicago's lakefront has moved both eastward with landfill and westward with erosion since man first arrived. The pier at the river mouth, which Jefferson Davis supervised in 1833 giving the city a harbor, brought far reaching changes. On the north side, sand piled up providing natural lake fill, creating what was eventually to be some of the most valuable real estate in the nation. On the south side, the shoreline began to erode. By 1850, the lake would invade Michigan Avenue, during storms, threatening the fashionable homes built there.

The City, without funds to provide a breakwater for the south shore, and unable to secure a Federal grant, turned to the railroads who were eager to secure right-of-way. In 1852, the Illinois Central built the breakwater in return for shoreline property. A century of land-filling operations followed.

The first substantial land fill operations were associated with the construction of access to Lincoln Park. Although Lincoln Park was designed by Swain Nelson to follow the natural hills and gullies left by the retreating glaciers, the beaches were extended by landfill operations continuing into this century.

A private citizen, George Wellington (Cap) Streeter, contributed to the landfill in the area now occupied by the $100,000,000 Hancock Center. His steamboat hit a sandbar and broke up 450 feet from shore in 1886; sand drifted about the boat. He invited building contractors to dump on his newly formed land, and thousands of tons of debris were hauled in from the north side where mansions were being erected. When authorities tried to evict Cap Streeter, he fought back; bloody battles ensued. Eventually Streeter was caught, tried for murder and imprisoned. Today, the Hancock Building rises from Streeterville Plaza; Streeter Drive winds near Olive Park at the Central Filtration Plant to Navy Pier.

Following Burnham's plan for Grant Park, extensive shoreline filling began in 1901 and continued to the present time, although most of the necklace of islands and lagoons planned by Burnham were never built. Between the world wars, over a billion dollars in landfill created commercial and recreational facilities along the lakeshore.

19. Streeterville, 1973
What was once Lake Michigan is now some of Chicago's - and the world's - most valuable real estate. Through landfill, Chicago moves eastward as evidenced by this stretch of Lake Shore Drive, and the real property extending to Michigan Avenue and the site of the John Hancock Building. This view is from the roof of the Lake Point Tower apartment building, located at the foot of Navy Pier.

19

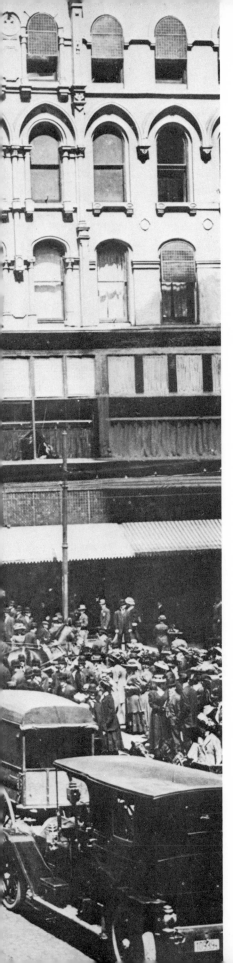

Streets

State and Madison, 1911
*Brick pavement withstands the heavy
traffic on the "world's busiest corner."
Today 750,000 people travel daily to the
Loop, which is only about half the number
that did in 1910, but today we have
490,000 motor vehicles, far out numbering
the 130,000 horse drawn carts and wagons
plus the 20,000 street cars of 1910.*

Paving The Prairie

Chicago is built on an old swamp of soft, impervious clay. In spring, melting snows slowly disappeared in the sun. With poor surface drainage, and a naturally high water table, Chicago was a sea of mud much of the year.

The first attempt at street construction took place in 1834 when South Water Street ran along the south bank of the river. The street was graded so that drainage from intersecting streets would flow across it into the river. Since the streets were nearly the same level as the river, horses and wagons splashed along in pursuit of commerce despite obstructions and inconvenience.

The earliest overland connections with the immediate region were by stage and prairie schooner on roads that were, at best uncertain, always uncomfortable, and often impassable in the spring and fall. One innovation which improved conditions somewhat in the 1840's, was the development of plank roads. With better roads came regular stagecoach service, first to Detroit and St. Louis and eventually to New York City.

The plank road idea was imported from Russia to Canada, where 500 miles of such roads were built between 1839 and 1849. The first plank road in this country was built in New York in 1846, and was very successful. Such roads spread westward, with construction mainly by plank road companies which collected tolls to cover the costs of construction, operation and maintenance.

In 1848, ten miles of an eight-foot wide plank road was built along the Barry Point Road from Chicago to what is now Riverside. It consisted of three-inch thick planks laid flat across two stringers that were embedded in the ground along the length of the road. The planks were not nailed to the stringers since the stringers were intended not to carry the weight, but merely to prevent tilting of the planks from wheel impacts while the ground was soft. The planks were expected to remain sound for many years by resting on a hard subgrade, well compacted to avoid air pockets and to keep water out.

Roads built later were graded to a width of 16 feet, providing a four-foot shoulder on each side for wagons to

1. Planked Road, 1830s
Poor drainage made quagmires of most of Chicago's streets, which were built only slightly above water level. Planked roads, made first of pine and later of oak, were the first attempt to provide passable roads. Shown here is the Frink and Walters firm which towered above all competitors in the Chicago area and for years enjoyed a practical monopoly in passenger transportation over a large portion of the middle west.

2. Retail Stores at 130 - 134 Lake Street, 1843
Busy Lake Street was the first street to be planked by the City in 1848, by order of the Common Council. This drawing shows the horse drawn water vendor splashing down the street. To fill their barrels, water vendors would simply back their horse up into Lake Michigan along the beach and dip water into the barrels.

3. Installing Nicholson Pavement (Drawing), 1859
The Nicholson patented pavement consisted of several layers of prepared surfaces including a subgrade board flooring covered with six-inch pine blocks. The joints were filled with tar and cinder or gravel. This pavement proved a substantial improvement over other street surfaces including boulder stone, limestone blocks, cobblestones and macadam. An 1867 court injunction prevented further use of this pavement by Chicago.

All photographs are on file with the Chicago Historical Society

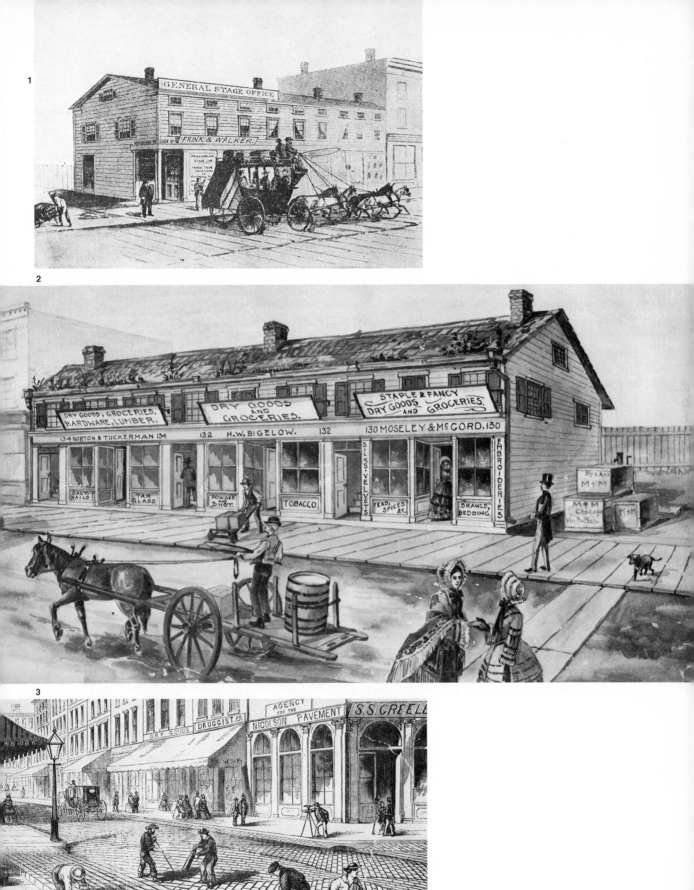

pass, and more durable oak planks replaced pine. Also ditches were dug along each side to drain off the water, and the earth dug out was used to make the road higher.

Under such circumstances, the plank roads were popular, and plank road companies were a booming business. Construction costs were about $2,000 per mile with toll gates five or six miles apart. With a toll charge of $2^1/_2$ cents per mile, the maximum allowable by State law, profits of from 14 per cent to as much as 40 per cent were realized. But, during flood times, many planks floated away. To avoid this loss, the planks sometimes were removed and stacked until drier weather. Water collecting under the planks allowed them to slip off the stringers and air to reach and decay the underside of the planks. Even oak planks lasted only from 10 to 12 years and maintenance and replacement reserves of $10.00 per mile per year proved to be inadequate.

The typical plank road was a convenience for one season, then the planks became warped by the sun until the riding quality was as bad as the old-fashioned roads. Travelers avoided using them, and finally inhabitants along the route took the planks for other uses. So, within less than 10 years the plank roads radiating out from Chicago were founded, flourished, and failed. Although the rural roads were private undertakings in which stockholders bore the loss, some streets in Chicago had also been planked by the City.

A variety of other materials were tried to surface the streets and roads in and around Chicago, including stone, cinders and whatever else was available. All these experiments failed as the surfacing materials disappeared into the mud within a year or two. Planking appeared still to be the only feasible solution and in January, 1848, the Common Council ordered the planking of Lake Street, 48 feet wide, from State Street to the South Branch of the river. The plan also established the intersection of State and Madison as the summit of a gravity-flow drainage system to carry sewage via bridged-over street gutters to the lake, the Main Branch and the South Branch of the river. Apparently there was not enough slope or water to make the scheme work and the stench of stagnant sewage became intolerable within a month after completion.

So, the City tried again by raising the grade of the main streets by two to six feet above natural ground level. This plan worked better and in 1850, Market Street (the present north-south section of Wacker Drive) was planked; also State, Clark, LaSalle, Wells and Madison streets; and the sewers on these streets were moved underground.

Street surfacing remained a principal problem for the next decade. Planking was a failure; and so were experiments with cable stones, block limestone, cinders and gravel. In the spring, for weeks streets were impassable and often principal thoroughfares were littered with abandoned wagons and drays.

4. Wacker Drive, 1973
Ancient autos begin tour of 25 Illinois cities as part of "Good Roads Day," a motorcade held in commemoration of the 1914 "Get Illinois out of the Mud" campaign.

5. Streetpaving on Clark Street at Madison
Workmen are shown installing a pavement designed by W. W. Boyington for use without charge for patent rights. Photograph was taken some time after the Fire of 1871.

6. Paved Washington Street, 1865
The Crosby Opera House, between Dearborn and State streets shows high curbed walks and good street surface. One of Chicago's first gas lights, installed in 1850, is shown in foreground. Telegraph poles are visible in background.

All photographs are on file with the Chicago Historical Society

4

48

6

This provided sport for local pranksters as indicated in the following excerpt from Bross' history:

"As the clerks had nothing to do, they would exercise their wits by putting boards from dry goods boxes in the holes where the last dray was dug out, with significant signs, as 'No Bottom Here,' 'The Shortest Road to China.' Sometimes one board would be nailed across another, and an old hat and coat fixed on it, with the notice 'On His Way to the Lower Regions.' In fact, there was no end to the fun; and jokes of the boys of that day . . ."

1857 ushered in a new era in street improvements, which by this time included lighting by gas lamps. In July, an engineering innovation finally set the street paving problem on more promising course—the first Nicholson pavement in the West was in Wells Street between South Water and Lake streets.

The Nicholson patented pavement consisted of excavating the earth to the proper depth, crown and grade, creating what is to this day referred to as a "subgrade," and laying thereon a flooring of one inch boards, generally laid lengthwise to the street. After mopping the floor boards with hot tar, pine blocks six inches high were placed on end on the coated floor boards, separated by one inch wide by three-inch high boards, known as "pickets" crosswise the street. The joints were then filled with tar and gravel or cinders.

The Nicholson pavement was a great step forward, but in a few years, the City was bothered by the "pickets" working up out of the joint, so modifications were tried omitting the pickets. In 1867, a court injunction restrained the City from building the original patented type of Nicholson pavement, and in 1868, a new design was developed by W. W. Boyinton of Chicago, without charge for patent rights. This variant consisted of one-inch by five-inch boards nailed on the flat, crosswise of the floor boards and bearing against the rows of seven inch high wood blocks. On the five-inch crossboards, wooden blocks six inches high and three inches wide were used. The resulting one-inch wide by six-inch deep spaces between the alternate rows of 6-inch and 7-inch high blocks were filled with gravel and tar as in the previous designs.

Finally, in 1869, the first use of a bituminous asphaltic concrete pavement was placed in small test pieces. Thus, about 100 years ago, the basic materials for constructing so-called "flexible" pavements were introduced. Since then, a great deal of work has been done in selecting and processing the materials used, testing and improving the subgrade, and developing more scientific designs and better construction methods required for modern pavements to handle heavier loads and high-speed traffic.

7. State Street, South from Lake Street, 1869
Horse drawn transit cars dominate the street scene in busy downtown Chicago. These wooden sidewalks were soon to add fuel to the fire which destroyed every building shown here. Gas streetlights are also prominent on both sides of the street.

8. South Park Avenue, 1892
Gas lights and tree shaded curbs mark this fashionable residential area of the last century shown at 32nd Street.

9. Grand Boulevard, 1892
Called Martin Luther King Drive today, Grand Boulevard was one of the major thoroughfares leading to Washington Park. One of the crucial elements of Chicago's park plan was the linking of the parks by paved tree-shaded boulevards.

All photographs are on file with the Chicago Historical Society

7

8

9

Lake Shore Drive

When Lincoln Park was established in 1864, work began on the construction of a road along the shoreline, a parkway, which followed the natural beauty of the lake rather than the fixed grid pattern of the city. Amid mud and frog ponds, work progressed slowly, inhibited by the lake which relentlessly battered and eroded the shoreline, and by the natural construction hazards of the time, roaming cattle. Eventually engineers mastered techniques of buttressing the roadway against the lake and as the city extended eastward by filling operations, Lake Shore Drive continued to the south.

By the 1880's, Lake Shore Drive was carrying larger amounts of traffic, not only to Lincoln Park but to the northern suburban communities as well. A description of the road then is still applicable today: *"One of the handsomest carriage ways to be found in the world."*

A variety of engineering accomplishments serve to provide the commuting motorist with a rapid transportation route and with an often exhilarating view of lake and skyline, while at the same time protecting the recreational value of Chicago's priceless lakefront. Engineers pioneered techniques for separating normal and road traffic from the park pedestrian pathways by making use of the first cloverleafs, now a common sight at expressway interchanges in all major cities. Extensive landscaping and innovative use of berms and earth mounds also softened the impact of sights and sounds of traffic from park areas.

Lane reversal mechanisms were another imaginative design feature incorporated in 1935 in the Drive. In an effort to reduce the road width and to provide maximum traffic flow, divisional fins were recessed in the pavement. By hydraulically activating the fins, a continous barrier eight inches high would project on the roadway. The lanes were reversed through the day to accomodate the heavy inbound traffic in the morning and outbound at night. The fins contained lighted lenses for night illumination. In this way, a 100-foot road width carries the traffic of a 170 foot width, at a savings not only in cost, but in lessening of visual obstruction to the lake and park regions.

10. Lake Shore Drive, 1890s
Paved beaches such as this one at the east end of High Bridge help hold back Lake Michigan from the path of Lake Shore Drive, one of the world's most scenic thoroughfares. Separated pedestrian grade crossings such as shown here illustrate early traffic design innovation permitting access to the lakefront by both vehicle and pedestrian.

11. Lake Shore Drive in Lincoln Park, 1936
Grade separation cloverleafs, now common throughout the nation, were pioneered here on Lake Shore Drive. Three such cloverleafs are visible adjacent to land fill harbor and beach area.

12. Pedestrian Bridge, 1968
Fast moving street traffic presents as formidable an obstacle for pedestrians as does a river. To separate pedestrians from vehicles, this beautiful pedestrian bridge was built over Lake Shore Drive at 51st Street in 1967. The graceful design won an Award of Merit in the American Institute of Steel Construction competition in 1967.

13. Lake Shore Drive, 1973
Tall condominiums, apartment houses and office buildings line Lake Shore Drive.

All photographs are on file with the Chicago Historical Society

10

11

BRYN MAWR AVE.

IRVING PARK BLVD.

12

13

Double-Decker Wacker Drive

"Make no little plans," Burnham wrote in his plan for the city. The replacement of old South Water street along the river by the two level, grade separated Wacker Drive must rank with the major achievements in city improvements anywhere.

Picturesque South Water Street was the first street in Chicago when the city was nothing more than an outpost in the wilderness. The first cabins of early settlers were built here. Ox-drawn wagons bringing immigrants to the settlement, and later farmers hauling produce to the soldiers in the Fort, all splashed along South Water. As the city grew, South Water became the public market and major food distribution center. It was a show place for the city, reeking with a fantastic mixture of odors and clamorous noises.

For a half century, South Water was also a kaleidoscopic nightmare for traffic cops, pedestrians and drivers, inadequate in providing street and loading access consistent with modern techniques in food distribution. Burnham's report wrote, *"South Water Street today is an economic waste; a burdensome charge on all the people; a drawback to Chicago's progress and obstructive to its prosperity."*

"The Plan for Chicago" called for the replacement of the old street with a double level ornamental drive: an upper level for general use, connecting with major streets and boulevards; the lower level, 25 feet wider than the upper level for commercial traffic, connecting to warehouses, boat and rail terminals and industrial sites. The concept of grade separation, in this case of removing pedestrian and routine traffic from the commercial flow was essential not only to relieve traffic congestion in the downtown area, but also to provide space for freight handling and warehousing under the upper level streets.

Essential as this plan was for providing a much needed solution to the problems of the time as well as for the future of the city, sentiment remained strong for the old street. Citizens groups challenged the right of these improvements to be made and residents of the market struggled to prevent adoption of the plan:

14. South Water Street, "Pre-Wacker Drive," about 1900
Granite cobblestones were necessary to withstand the ceaseless pounding of horse carts in what was Chicago's principal market. These business enterprises were relocated in 1925 for the construction of Wacker Drive. Photograph looks west from Dearborn.

15. Wacker Drive, 1929
The area once intended to be used for loading wharves for river traffic on the lower level is now the scene of parking lots for automobiles which would have astonished the street's architect, Daniel Burnham. The automobile age is generally considered to have begun in 1903, the year of the organization of the Ford Motor Company, and coincidentally the time of the Chicago Plan, adopted by the City in 1910. Today, lower Wacker at rush hour provides an important artery for Chicago's automobile traffic, lessening traffic congestion in a way the street's designers would not have imagined; today riverfront parks are replacing the parking areas along the river.

16. Plaque
The completion of Wacker Drive was marked by this 1926 bronze plaque illustrating historic South Water Street from 1824 to 1924.

All photographs are on file with the Chicago Historical Society

15

16

*"They want to stay where Nature put
them, here on the old waterfront".
"We were here first; we belong and have no place to go."*

Ultimately, the aging market was replaced and over 8,000 property owners were compensated for the displacement. The market was relocated two miles away, eliminating nearly 20% of the total vehicle traffic to the Loop.

All buildings between the street and the river were demolished and replaced by the double-decked drive. The completion of the drive set off a construction boom in high rise buildings bordering the river, with the Civic Opera Building rising to dominate the district and across the river; the world's largest building at the time, the Merchandise Mart was erected. Finally, despite the protest of many to preserve the historic old street designation, the City Council renamed the thoroughfare Wacker Drive, in honor of Charles H. Wacker, a civic and cultural leader whose energetic public relations work was responsible for the massive public support and financial backing for the Chicago Plan.

Wacker Drive was completed in 1926, although additional improvements and extensions have kept pace with the times. Today, attractive riverfront parks grace the lower level at LaSalle and more are planned along the river for the extension leading to Lake Shore Drive. More than 30,000 pedestrians walk the nearby Loop area near LaSalle, the financial heart of the Midwest. Closeby office workers and visitors frequent these small riverfront malls, so inviting as a meeting place for relaxation and enjoyment.

17. Wacker Drive Extension 1973
Wacker Drive is being continued from Michigan Avenue to Lake Shore Drive. The bridge at the mouth of the river was designed to carry a second level of traffic as does the Michigan Avenue bridge. Plans are also underway to eliminate the S-curve which slows traffic to 30 miles per hour.

All photographs are on file with the Chicago Historical Society

17

Alterations and Dissent

All great urban planners share the ability to find solutions to the pressing needs of the day in such a way that the completed work becomes a component of a great, single entity: the well-ordered, convenient, unified and dynamic urban center. Chicago's plan achieved this goal in a very practical way which accounts for the enthusiastic acceptance. Those individuals displaced by the renovations are however less than enthusiastic.

The Chicago Plan called for widening and extending several major streets; several were completed, notably LaSalle Street, Roosevelt Road with the great viaduct across the industrial zone, and Michigan Avenue.

Michigan Avenue was known as the *"The Magnificent Mile"* and seemed destined to be one of the great commercial boulevards of the world. However, within a few hundred yards of the river, the street suddenly necked down to a narrow sixty-six feet, before turning at the water's edge toward Rush Street. Traffic could only move across the Rush Street Bridge, a small structure which carried 77 percent of the automobiles and 26 percent of the commercial vehicles coming into the Loop from the North Side.

In 1914, the people voted a bond issue to begin widening the street and to build a new bridge. Many property owners contested the proposed improvement, and called it a project for *"automobile owners' and the rich."* The City, backed by the Plan Commission, fought the case through the courts and won. Fronts of huge buildings were cut away, and all obstruction cleared away. Over 8700 property settlements were made before litigation was finally finished. When the project was completed, the owners found to their amazement that in addition to the damages they received, their property was worth several times as much as it was worth before. On May, 1929, a large public crowd greeted the street widening and bridge opening ceremony. The Michigan Avenue Bridge has virtually become a trademark of the Chicago scene, and is one of the most widely photographed bridges in existence today.

Not all proposed modifications succeeded. Halsted Street is

one such example. When the Plan Commission urged that Halsted be widened the residents objected, preferring to believe that somehow congestion would ease and they could be spared the relocation inconvenience of disruption by the proposed street widening. The plan was abandoned. Years later, when traffic increased beyond all expectations, the street was often blocked off entirely and trade slackened. The property owners then petitioned for the same street widening which they had previously refused. However, so many new buildings had been erected that the cost had become prohibitive and the steet modifications were never carried out. This turn of events, unfortunate though it may be, illustrates an occasion when the sentiment and considerations of immediate convenience outweighed future contingencies. Had these same factors prevailed in the Michigan Avenue modifications, it is unlikely that Michigan Avenue would today be one of the world's magnificent retail boulevards.

18. Michigan Avenue, 1860s
Always a beautiful street, this view looking north from Congress Hall shows the grain elevators along the river and the Illinois Central terminal in the center of the picture as they looked before the Great Fire of 1871.

19. Widening of Michigan Avenue, 1916
The dotted line marks the section of buildings to be removed to widen Michigan Avenue, in this photograph looking north from Randolph Street. This Public Works project, of great inconvenience to the businessmen and customers alike, resulted in the creation of one of the world's great commercial boulevards.

20. Widening of North LaSalle Street, 1936
To provide additional connecting arteries to the Loop, a bridge was built at LaSalle Street and the street was widened in anticipation of the increased traffic flow. Projects such as this, although a disadvantage and inconvenience to those directly involved, are of lasting benefit to the city and are one of the reasons why Chicago is one of the few major urban centers to maintain a viable central business district.

21. Michigan Avenue, 1973
Looking north toward the Ontario intersection is the fashionable North Michigan Avenue commercial center.

22. Michigan Avenue, 1896
The end of the 19th century saw the last of the fashionable townshouses in the central area such as these. After this photograph was taken, these buildings were demolished to make way for new hotels and office buildings.

All photographs are on file with the Chicago Historical Society

18

19

20

22

21

Street Lighting

Lamps date to the earliest vestiges of man, when oil or animal fat was burned for illumination; man, without knowledge of fire, is unknown. These lamps date to earliest man in the Mousterian age, which marked the culmination of the Neanderthal man. Terracotta lamps of 8,000 BC can be seen today in museums. By 1000 BC an advance in lighting efficiency was obtained by using a vegetable fibre oil lamp and by 100 BC the Romans enclosed the light source making the first lanterns. These first lanterns were made of perforated, cylindrical horns. True candles, made of coated, flax threads, came into existence about the same time; although pure wax candles are credited to the Phoenicians around 400 AD.

The earliest record of street lighting, as a result of community effort, begins in 200 AD when lamps were hung from each door in Rome. In 1630, Paris had three fixed lanterns, and in 1408 lanterns were ordered placed in each street during a period of unrest. In 1775, polished metal reflectors were developed to control the direction of the light rays, which is the essence of effective street lighting.

Gas for street lighting was first demonstrated in London in 1807, and the first municipal street lighting service went into operation in 1823 when more than 7,000 gas lamps lit London streets. The concept and technique soon spread throughout the world. The discovery of the electric arc in 1808 led eventually to the enclosed arc lamp, the heated filament lamp and the metal vapor lamps of today.

By the time Chicago developed as a municipality, gas street lighting was common-place in most metropolitan regions. By 1857 gas lamps were in operation through Chicago, rising to a peak of 36.853 by the end of the century.

Chicago's electric street lighting had its beginning on Christmas Eve, 1887, when 125 arc lamps were placed in service to light the bridges crossing the Chicago River. Power was provided by city owned steam-electric generating stations. Starting in 1907, cheap electric power became available to the City, supplied by the water driven generators in Lockport, Illinois, operated by the Metropolitan Sanitary

23. Chicago's Oldest Street Light
Originally a flaming arc lamp before a modern mercury vapor lamp was installed, this 1892 fixture was moved from Cottage Grove and 29th Street to the site of the Chicago Historical Society at Clark and Chicago Avenue in 1959. For a view of the original illumination unit, see the flaming arc light on page 12.

24. Columbia Base, 1900–1917

25. Brenner Post, 1898–1912

26. Arc Lamp, 1898–1905

27. Standard Ornamental Gas Lamp, 1915

28. Gas Lamp, 1923

29. Standard Incandescent Lamp, 1912–1925

30. Gasoline Lamp, Standard, 1915

31. Ogden Avenue Improvement, 1923

32. Gas Post Converted to Tungsten Lamp, 1923

33. "Chicago Beautiful" Post, 1923

34. Popular 1920's Harp Fixture Removed in 1950's

All photographs are on file with the Chicago Historical Society

23 24 25 26 27 28

29 30 31 32 33 34

District. By 1908, a total of 50,000 gasoline and gas lamps had been reduced to 26,000 in number, and 8200 electric arc lamps were in operation. In 1910, a program for the installation of an additional 10,000 electric street lights within a four year period was initiated. In 1912, metallized carbon and long burning flame arc lamps were introduced. A total of 862 of these lamps, in alba, round ball globes were mounted on posts previously used for gas fixtures. In addition, some 1,166 alternating series arcs were changed to the flame arc type.

The first tungsten incandescent lamps appeared in 1914 on Chicago streets and were adopted as the standard. During 1917, all flame arc lamps were changed to nitrogen filled, tungsten, incandescent lamps. The first lamps were of only 100 candlepower; later, in 1924, work began on installation of 6,548 new concrete posts in residential districts having 250 candlepower units for each lamp. During the subsequent years, a series of bond issues were voted in for new and improved lighting until by the end of 1932, Chicago had a total of 93,374 electric street lights, representing the largest municipal electric street lighting system in the world.

Over the years, improvements in the technology of illumination have changed the appearance of the fixtures. The large base area of the standards which formerly housed the ballasts are no longer in use, since modern fixtures incorporate the ballast in the lamp unit. Mercury vapor lamps have appeared, and today the new high pressure sodium lamps are being installed as need and funds permit. Perhaps the most striking program was the $130 million alley lighting program between 1947 to 1965. During one six month period, a total of 45,000 lights were installed, a figure which has never been equaled before or since anywhere. A greater volume of favorable public reaction was evoked over this alley lighting program than any other program in the history of City government.

35

35. Heavy Arterial Lighting June, 1971
North Halsted Street Viaduct is shown with mercury vapor installation for heavy traffic.

36. Alley Lighting
The success of the alley lighting program is shown in this typical scene between Francisco and Richmond looking south from 64th Street.

37. Residential Lighting April, 1968
Mercury vapor lamps now light 100 percent of all Chicago neighborhoods. The site shown is Bell Avenue looking north from 98th Street.

38. East Wacker Drive December, 1969
New mercury vapor lighting installed along Wacker Drive.

39. Night-time Neighborhood, 1968
The high quality of the 20,000 lumen mercury vapor lighting is evident in this scene at Central Park Avenue looking north from Augusta Blvd.

All photographs are on file with the Chicago Historical Society

36

37

38

39

63

Waterworks

4

Sunset at the Filtration Plant, 1971
*Olive Park, enjoyable for picnicking,
fishing and sight seeing during the day is
endowed with a beautiful view of the
skyline at sunset.*

The Chicago City Hydraulic Company

The first public water supply was a well dug in 1834 in the vicinity of Rush and Kinzie streets. The supply was insufficient for the growing demand, so private vendors hauled water in carts, first from the river, then from the lake when the former became too contaminated. The lake waters at the shore line soon became polluted and the need for a better water supply became so acute that the State Legislature granted a 70-year charter to the Chicago Hydraulic Company, a private enterprise, to build and operate a water works. Due to financial problems arising from the 1839 financial crash, the company did not begin construction until 1840.

When the new water works was activated in 1842, it provided an occasion for civic celebration. The plant, at Lake Street near the present Michigan Avenue, was designed to draw water from a wooden pipe extending about 150 feet into the lake. When the boiler was fired up starting the 25 H.P. pump, many citizens watched with great anticipation. As the first trickle of *"pure fresh water"* flowed from the pipe and quickly developed into a gushing stream, a great cheer went up.

By 1851 the population of the city had increased to 35,000 persons. It became obvious that private resources were no longer adequate to supply sufficient potable water for the city's needs, consequently, the legislature gave Chicago a charter for a public water works system, creating the Chicago City Hydraulic Company.

William J. McAlpine, Chief Engineer, was directed to develop a water system adequate to the current and anticipated needs of the city. The plan presented by McAlpine in 1851 called for a system with capacity to supply a city of 162,000 persons. Although the estimated figure anticipated a five-fold growth by 1875, it missed the mark by a full decade when that population was reached before 1865. On March 2, 1852, at the regular municipal elections, the voters approved the adoption of the water works proposition following the election, the City negotiated the sale of $400,000 in revenue bonds. Construction began in the summer of 1852 and in February, 1854, the work was completed and the new water supply

1. Private System, 1842
The first water intake was located only 150 feet into the lake and failed to meet the growing city's needs. The site is at Lake and Michigan avenues.

2. First Public Waterworks, 1854
The original water system consisted of a small pumping station and three reservoirs.

3. Original Waterworks, 1854
Chicago's first municipal owned waterworks began serving the city's 35,000 people in February of 1854, replacing the privately owned City Hydraulic Company's system which had a capacity to service a population of only 4500. The pump of the new system operated just nine hours a day and not at all on Sundays except in case of fire. A larger pump, 12 MGD, replaced the original 8 MGD pump in July 1857, but the capacity could not keep up with the demand. Further, the increasing prevalence of waterborne disease resulting from lake pollution made it mandatory that a new system, one having an intake much farther out then the 600 feet of this early system, be developed.

4. Water Tower and Pumping Station, 1870
The Water Tower is shown at its present location on Michigan Avenue at a time when Lake Michigan's shores were close to the pumping station. The first two-mile crib is easily visible in the distance. The ornamental tower enclosed the long water pipe necessary to prevent surges in the line from the older reciprocating pumps. Today's rotary pumps do not require these tall towers.

All photographs are on file with the Chicago Historical Society

1

2

4

3

initiated.

The new intake, built of timber with a three by four foot opening, reached out into the lake about 600 feet and terminated in a brick suction well. The mouth of the intake was protected by a semi-circular breakwater of timber and stone. The pumping station, located at Pine Street (now Michigan Avenue) and Chicago Avenue, was built of brick with an Italian architectural motif. It housed an 8 million gallons per day single action pump engine. Its tower enclosed both the smoke stack and stand pipe. The distribution system consisted of about nine miles of cast iron pipe and one iron reservoir, some eighty feet above ground level.

Within three years, the pumping capacity of the system was insufficient. A second pumping station of 12 M.G.D. capacity was installed and became operational in July, 1857.

By 1861, the river once again contaminated the supply from the lake. The increasing prevalence of typhoid fever and dysentery made it obvious that the water intake would again have to be placed at a greater distance from shore. Furthermore, there was already need for a still greater daily supply of water. The solution came in the form of one of the great engineering achievements of the century.

5

The Water Tower

The responsibility for development of another water supply fell to the Chief Engineer, E.H. Chesbrough. Since his arrival in Chicago, he had frequently served as consultant to the water commissioners and was thoroughly familiar with the existing system. Chesbrough immediately proposed that a five-foot diameter water supply tunnel be dug 60 feet below the bottom of the lake to a distance of 10,567 feet—almost two miles, where a water intake crib would be placed.

The drastic proposal was met with doubt and criticism. Again Chesbrough prevailed, despite restrictions imposed by the Civil War, and the Council authorized the project. The work commenced on the land shaft at Chicago Avenue on March 17, 1864. Work on the tunnel progressed day and night, averaging about 12 feet each 24 hours. Despite many difficulties encountered in boring through Lake Michigan's subterrain—including gas pockets, quicksand, and boulders—no serious mishaps occurred.

Meanwhile, a pentagonal crib built of wood was successfully launched July 24, 1865. With the crib securely in place on the lake bottom and pumped dry, an intake shaft was sunk inside. Tunneling from there was pursued and at 3:40 p.m. on November 30, 1866, the two work headings beneath were joined with a misalignment of only seven inches.

The final masonry stone was placed on December 6, one and one-half miles from shore where the shafts had met. As the mayor put the marble block in place, he said, "Now, gentlemen, in behalf of the City of Chicago, I place the last stone in this great tunnel—the wonder of America and the world."

The following March, the $465,000 tunnel was tested and on the 25th was formally dedicated. That day it was filled once more and clear, fresh water was pumped to the city. Franc B. Wilkie, a local newspaper man wrote: *"The cleansing properties of the new water are wonderful. Children whose faces have been washed in it have been lost and never found. Their mothers cannot recognize them. It is proposed to establish a place where lost children may be gathered, and where only the old water will be used in their ablutions. In*

5. The Old Water Tower, 1972
This picturesque water tower of castellated Gothic design, erected in 1867, symbolizes today the engineering achievements of one of the first major projects of the City's Public Works Department under the direction of the City Engineer, Ellis F. Chesbrough. Ridiculed as a visionary scheme by some, the system included the unprecedented construction of a subterranean tunnel sixty feet below the lake surface and stretching two miles out from shore. The cost of the tunnel was $457,845 considerably over the bid price of $315,139 in 1863. When bids were placed, common labor was $1.25 per hour, which was considered high at that time. But as the Civil War progressed, inflationary pressures brought higher salaries. The finished cost of the tunnel was $18.45 per lineal foot. Portions of this tunnel system, still considered as one of the engineering wonders of the world, are still in use today.

All photographs are on file with the Chicago Historical Society

time, it is expected that many young children, whom nobody now knows, will be recognized by their parents."

While the elevation of Chicago and its outstanding sewerage system had made Chesbrough nationally renowned, the water tunnel and works completed in 1869 brought him international fame. Chicago's water supply system, now vastly enlarged and improved but fundamentally the same as this prototype, is visited and studied by engineers and students from all over the world.

During the early part of 1869, the building for the new pumping works and the imposing water tower, (now famous for having survived the Great Fire of 1871), were completed. During 1870-71, four tunnels were constructed under the North and South branches of the river to supply the West Side with water.

It is interesting and revealing to note that when the City planned its first public water works in 1851, it was then estimated that by 1871, the City would require an enormous 4.75 million gallons per day. When that year had passed, however, the city was supplying its citizens and industry with 23.5 million gallons daily! One hundred years later, the daily design capacity of Chicago's filtered water works were capable of supplying the city and suburban clients with well over l.4 billion gallons per day!

The primary concern of engineers continued to revolve around the dilemma of supplying an increasing demand for water. At first the answer consisted of increasing the capacity of the original pumping system with the installation of additional engines to draw more water from the two-mile crib at the Chicago Avenue pumping station. This single station, however, was not able to provide sufficient quantity of water at adequate pressure for the entire growing city.

The second tunnel, seven feet in diameter, was built from the two-mile crib, under both lake and city, to 22nd Street and Ashland Avenue where another station with two pumps of 15 MGD was established. This station went into operation in 1876. The two stations served the city for about a decade. Another water system, commenced in 1887, embraced the Harrison Street and Fourteenth Street stations, which were connected by tunnels to a new crib placed four miles from shore opposite Roosevelt Road. The pumping stations of this network went into operation in 1890.

6–10. Tunnel Construction, 1866
Newspapers and weekly magazines vied to bring to the public the story of the construction of the tunnels under Lake Michigan. The titles of these drawings explain the activity:
"Going Down in the Tunnel Shaft"
"Railroading under Lake Michigan"
"Turn-table in the Supply Chambers"
"Workman Constructing the Upper Arch of the Tunnel"
"The Crib of Lake End of the Tunnel, where the Pure Water is Taken from the Bottom of Lake Michigan,Two Miles from Shore"

11. "Old Sally", 1903
The first municipal owned pumping station engine, nick-named affectionately "Old Sally", was installed in 1853. A vertical condensing steam engine with a single acting pump of 8 MGD capacity, this pump served the city faithfully for over 50 years.

12. Cruise to the Cribs, 1973
The tug James J. Versluis approaches the Edward F. Dunne and 68th Street cribs some three miles from shore. The 68th Street Crib was built in 1893 for Chicago's Columbian Exposition. The tug transports and services the crews manning the Harrison-Dever and the Dunne-68th Street Crib which act as water intake for Chicago's two filtration plants. The two double cribs each have four tenders on duty at all times with the tenders serving seven hour shifts. The tug supplies the cribs twice each week.

13. The James J. Versluis, 1973
Built at the Sturgeon Bay shipyard in 1957, the Versluis is 83 feet long with 23 foot beam and a top speed of about 14 mph. Operated by the Department of Public Works, the tug services the water cribs, breaks ice in winter, and performs maintenance duty on the Chicago River. Once a week, biochemists from the filtration plants use the Versluis to take them to one or more of the 84 water sampling stations in the lake for bacterial analysis and chemical testing.

All photographs are on file with the Chicago Historical Society

The South Water Filtration Plant

Pure, sparkling clear water requires filtration, even from the purest natural sources. While Chicago's waterworks provided a water quality considered excellent at the turn of the century, small fishes were known on occasion to find their way into the intake. And even though Chicago did not contaminate the lake after construction of the Sanitary Canal and processing plants, the growing communities surrounding the area were of concern. Chicago inaugurated the use of chlorination in 1912, and by 1916 water at every one of Chicago's pumping stations was being sterilized by chlorination.

Scientists have long known how to produce chemically pure water from any water source. The first successful filtration plants were built by James Simpson in 1829 on the Thames River, London. The problem for Chicago was how to design a plant which would process the vast quantities needed for Chicago, and which would operate economically. To study this problem, engineers built an experimental filtration plant in 1928. Based on these studies, plans were prepared for a major, permanent installation. Construction on the South Water Filtration plant began in 1938 under a $5,500,000 Federal grant.

Owing to World War II priorities, the plant was not put into full operation until 1947. Today, after a total investment of $50,000,000, and with continued expansion and improvement, the plant serves some 2,000,000 people at a rated capacity of 480 million gallons a day, with a possible peak capacity of 850 million gallons per day, of pure, palatable, sparkling clear water.

Making Lake Michigan's water pure and sparkling is a many-step process. It includes bringing the water into the plant, testing and controlling the intake, treating it with chemicals, removing impurities, storage and pumping to tunnels leading to pumping stations. Careful control through sensitive instrumentation and computer analysis insure high quality and reduce cost of operation.

Chicago's South Water Filtration Plant was the largest in the world at the time of construction. Today it is the second largest, second to the newer sister plant on the near-north shore, the Central Filtration Plant.

14. South Water Filtration Plant

15. The William E. Dever Crib, June, 1965
The Carter Harrison Crib was built about three-quarters of a mile northeast of the two-mile Crib to meet the increased needs arising from annexations to Chicago in 1889; the Harrison Crib and tunnel system was completed in 1900. The newest crib, the William E. Dever, was built in 1934, adjacent to the Harrison Crib. Another crib, also approximately three miles from shore and just to the north of the Harrison-Dever cribs is the Wilson Crib. This crib was floated into position in 1915 but the tunnel system was not completed until 1918. Today the crib is maintained on a stand-by basis.

16. 68th Street and Dunne Cribs, June 1965
When the city of Hyde Park was annexed in 1889, Chicago obtained a six-foot tunnel with submerged intake a mile from shore, but the quality of water was unsatisfactory. In order to improve this condition and furnish additional water for the Fair of 1893, the City undertook development of the 68th Street Crib located nearly three miles from shore. Adjacent to this Crib is the Edward F. Dunne Crib, put into service in December 1911, to supply the Southwest Lake and Land Tunnel system. This tunnel was the first lake tunnel constructed through rock, the earlier tunnels being in clay.

17. Flow Diagram
Showing water to consumer.

72

14

15

16

17

TYPICAL FLOW DIAGRAM OF WATER from LAKE TO YOU

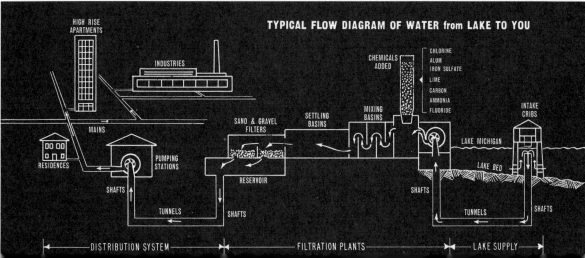

HIGH RISE
APARTMENTS

INDUSTRIES

CHEMICALS
ADDED

CHLORINE
ALUM
IRON SULFATE
LIME
CARBON
AMMONIA
FLUORIDE

SAND & GRAVEL
FILTERS

SETTLING
BASINS

MIXING
BASINS

INTAKE
CRIBS

MAINS

LAKE MICHIGAN

RESIDENCES

PUMPING
STATIONS

RESERVOIR

LAKE BED

SHAFTS

TUNNELS

SHAFTS

SHAFTS

SHAFTS

TUNNELS

SHAFTS

DISTRIBUTION SYSTEM

FILTRATION PLANTS

LAKE SUPPLY

18

19

20

21

18. West Side Pumping Station, 1874
The conflagration of the Great Fire of 1871 so damaged the machinery of the new station as to put it out of service for eight days. This, together with a break in the water main crossing the river and an increasing demand for water service on the west side, resulted in a decision to build a new tunnel and pumping station to serve the west side. The second tunnel, built to the original two-mile crib, was begun in 1872 and finished in 1874; it crossed the city diagonally, terminating at the new pumping station at Ashland and Blue Island Avenues, now 22nd Street. Because of problems of interference with deep foundations and pilings for large buildings, this tunnel was abandoned in 1909 when the Blue Island Avenue Tunnel was put in service. This tunnel, Chicago's first long concrete tunnel, was dewatered in 1932 for the first time in 23 years and found to be in good physical condition.

19. Aerial View of South Water Filtration Plant

20. The Lake View Pumping Station, 1967
The newest of Chicago's pumping stations was built on the old Lake View site; the new station, built at a cost of $1.4 million, has a 105 million gallon per day capacity. During 1972-73, all pumping stations were converted in the interests of reducing air pollution, from coal as a source of fuel for steam, to natural gas.

21. Pumping Station Interior
The dedication ceremonies of the Lakeview Pumping Station are in progress in this photograph.

22. Pumping and Tunnel System
Nearly one billion gallons of water are pumped each day through Chicago's 4,000 miles of water mains; these mains are supplied by 73 miles of water tunnels.

All photographs are on file with the Chicago Historical Society

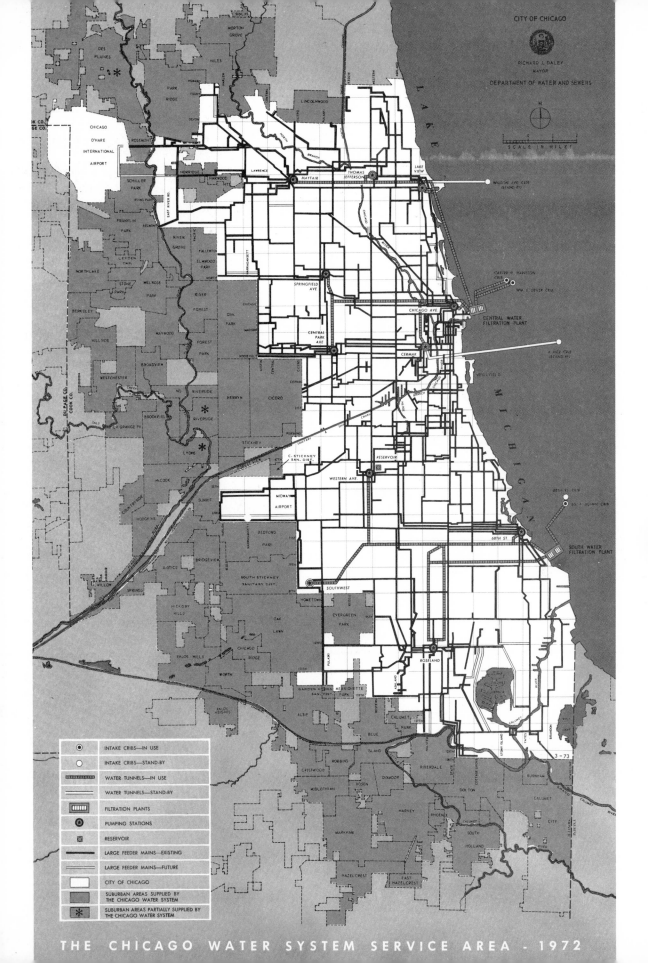

THE CHICAGO WATER SYSTEM SERVICE AREA - 1972

The Central Water Filtration Plant

A new era in engineering dawned about the time a new filtration plant was to be designed for the north side. Engineers, together with urban planners and scientists of all specialties, were becoming concerned with the effects of their work on the total quality of life. A concept developed where projects were considered not just in terms of the concrete needs of the moment, but in terms of future contingencies, and the total needs of the community.

The design and construction of the Central Water Filtration Plant was one of the first achievements of the interdisciplinary concept. Engineers, using the experience and knowledge of the filtration plant to the south, designed the world's largest plant, capable of producing 960 million gallons each day, or at peak operation, 1700 million gallons each day. Architects, social planners and urban scientists cooperated to produce a facility which was an outstanding contribution to Chicago's beautiful lakefront. The building elevation is purposely kept low and unobstructive, landscaped with hundreds of bushes, trees and plants. Five circular fountains, symbolic of the five Great Lakes, are featured in the recreational park area; jet sprays reach as high as 105 feet. At night, colored lights directed against the fountains provide viewing enjoyment. The park has walks, benches and an observation platform for viewing the city's skyline.

In the main foyer of the administration building, a massive bas-relief bronze sculpture "Hymn to Water" depicts the drama of water as the sustaining force in life.

While this plant is a technological triumph of our time, it is, in addition, an integral part of community life, providing recreational and cultural stimulus as well as visual pleasure.
"There went up a mist from the earth, and watered the whole face of the ground. And the Lord God formed man of the dust of the ground, and breathed into his nostrils the breath of life; and man became a living soul." (Genesis 2:6, 7)

23. Central Water Filtration Plant, 1972
The Central Water Filtration Plant, the world's largest, provides up to 1700 million gallons of pure water each day for Chicago and 75 surrounding communities, in addition to enhancing the recreational use of the lakefront. The facility buildings are low in elevation to prevent obstruction of lakeview from shoreline. Five circular fountains, symbolic of the five Great Lakes, are featured in the recreational park area; jet sprays reach as high as 105 feet. The park also has walks, benches, grassy expanses for picnics and an observation platform for viewing the city's skyline.

24. Administration Building, 1972
The Central Water Filtration Plant's water-theme of revitalization and growth are evident not only in Chicago's panorama, but in the execution of the plant's landscaping.
The Outstanding Civil Engineering Achievement Award of Merit, 1965, was awarded the Chicago Central Filtration Plant in a national competition conducted by the American Society of Civil Engineers.

25a. Bas-Relief, 1972
Water as an essential of Life, as well as a staple of urban growth, is depicted in Milton Horn's 6,500 pound bronze relief entitled, "Hymn to Water." The 24 foot 3 inch relief, an artistic creation par excellence, took two and one half years to complete and hangs in the main foyer of the Central Water Filtration Plant's administration building. The sculptor, Milton Horn, stands beside his work.

25b. Detail, "Hymn to Water"
This detail symbolizes the creation of man by a loving and compassionate Creative Force shown emerging from clouds, fire and mist. Other figures in the sculpture include the sun drawing up a rising column of water laden with life, the moon exerting tidal waves that thunder and beat against the shore forming its rugged contours, the whale, and the symbolic tree of life. There is day and night, and the mystery that transcends mankind and the measure of time.

23

24

25a

25b

Sewers

5

The Underflow Project 1973
*The massive Chicago Underflow is shown
under construction. When completed, this
system will be capable of storing flood
waters from a 375 square mile area
including Chicago and 56 suburbs.*

Elevating the City

The swamp on which Chicago is built provided a natural environment essentially hostile to human habitation. Inherent sanitation problems were imposed by a flat, poorly drained prairie having a high water table. No sewer system developed anywhere in the world could deal with these problems. Chicago's solution was daring and imaginative; when finished, it was designated as one of the seven modern engineering wonders of the United States.

By 1854, Chicago had four miles of closed sewer system at a depth of 5 to 8 feet below the surface of the principal street. These crudely constructed triangular-shaped oak structures were placed below the centerlines of the planked-paved streets. Because of the lack of elevation, the system did not drain properly and waterborne diseases were common. In 1854, 5.6% of the population — one in eighteen — died of typhoid. To combat this growing threat, Chicago sought advice from world experts. One such authority, Ellis Sylvester Chesbrough, renowned for his work in Boston and London, accepted the position of Chief Engineer for the City of Chicago, ending the Sewer Commission's search for the "most competent engineer of our time." Chesbrough immediately drew up the first comprehensive sewer system undertaken by any major city in this country.

Complaining that Chicago's existing privy vaults and drainage sluices were *"abominations that should be swept away as speedily as possible,"* Chesbrough presented a daring plan. He suggested that Chicago's mired streets be raised 12 to 16 feet so as to give sufficient elevation to build sewers that would drain into the river and lake by gravity flow. This generated still another city-wide furor. In response to the consternation of property owners, the Council passed a compromise ordinance which called for raising the street grade only four feet. Undaunted, Chesbrough sought additional elevation, and the next administration, under the leadership of colorful six-foot-six "Long John" Wentworth, gave the civil engineer three more feet. The event inspired a popular couplet: *The grade was raised by Mayor Dyer, and*

1. House Moving Advertisement, 1859
Many owners chose to move to outlying areas when the grade was raised. House moving became a lucrative enterprise.

2. Raising a Chicago Hotel, 1857
This engraving, titled "A New American Invention: Raising an Hotel in Chicago," described the raising of Briggs House, located at the northeast corner of Randolph and Wells streets. To raise the grade, solid masonry hotels were lifted four and a half feet and new foundations placed underneath in such an orderly fashion that business could proceed without interruption.

All photographs are on file with the Chicago Historical Society

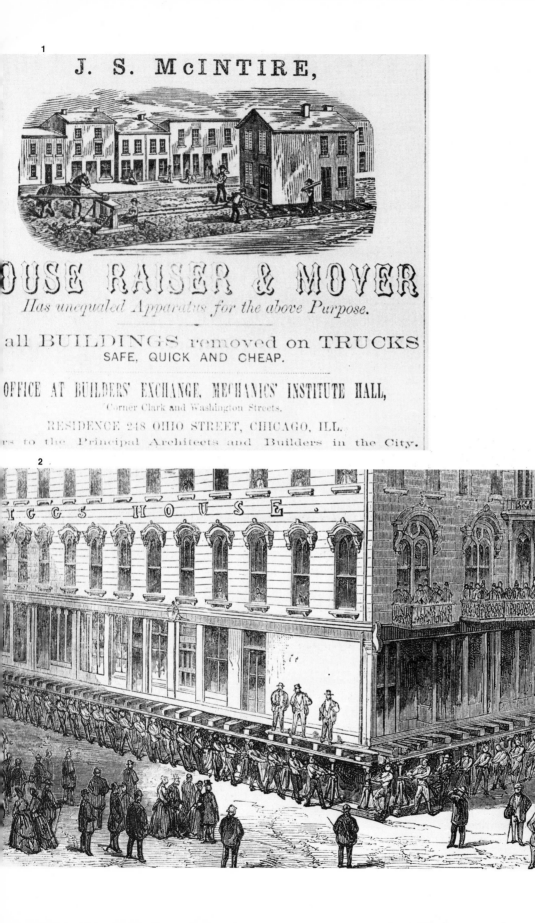

1

J. S. McINTIRE,

OUSE RAISER & MOVER

Has unequaled Apparatus for the above Purpose.

all BUILDINGS removed on TRUCKS
SAFE, QUICK AND CHEAP.

OFFICE AT BUILDERS' EXCHANGE, MECHANICS' INSTITUTE HALL,
Corner Clark and Washington Streets.

RESIDENCE 248 OHIO STREET, CHICAGO, ILL.

rs to the Principal Architects and Builders in the City.

2

IGGS HOUSE.

'Long John' made it three feet higher.

Although Chesbrough was able to get the streets elevated only about one-half as much as he wanted, it was enough. He was able to design a sewer system that worked. The drainage area was bounded by Division Street on the north, Reuben (now Ashland) on the west, North Street (now 16th Street) on the south, and by Lake Michigan. Since this required the sewers to be designed for a flatter grade, they could not maintain the velocity of flow necessary to be self-cleansing. Therefore, Chesbrough had to rely on adding water to flush periodically, or on hand-cleaning the sewers, both of which in the long run would be more expensive.

This plan was adopted by the Sewerage Board and presented to the Council on December 31, 1855. The public was alarmed about endangering the health of the city by sewers discharging into the river, but Chesbrough allayed their fears by pointing out that water from the lake could be introduced to purify the river.

In 1856, six miles of sewers were built. In the winter of 1856, the Council sent Chesbrough to Europe to study urban drainage systems there. He returned convinced that his original plan was best for Chicago. So, again with the help of Mayor Wentworth, he got four more feet of elevation of the streets, and five miles more of sewers were built in 1857. While Chesbrough's sewers improved sanitary conditions, havoc was wrought at homes, shops, and buildings where the streets rose nearly to the second floor. The occupants couldn't see across the street and to cross a thoroughfare or pass from one block to another involved climbing up and down steeply pitched stairs and ladders.

Various propositions were made to remedy this new problem. One was to fill the depressed land sites, making first floors into basements and second floors into main floors. Another suggested approach was to tear the city down, regrade it, and then rebuild. A third solution, for some with small structures, was simply to move their house or shop on rollers to another site beyond the regraded area.

At this time, another imaginative engineer from New England appeared on the Chicago scene. His name was George M. Pullman, about to become a manufacturer of railroad cars and later the founder of a planned industrial town. He thought the solution was relatively simple—just raise the buildings and put new foundations under them. Pullman was soon the laughing stock of the city as he was ridiculed for his impossible and insane scheme.

A few building owners, including the Tremont House management, were willing to give Pullman an opportunity to prove his point. The engineer promptly ordered one hundred turn-screw jacks from the East and when they were delivered, he hired a laborer to man each one of them. Within weeks the Tremont House was elevated to the new street level without disrupting its hotel operation! One guest said that the only reason he suspected something strange was going on is that each morning the front stairs of the building were at a different angle than the day before.

Having demonstrated that the outlandish was feasible, raising buildings and houses soon become fashionable, and the elevation of Chicago became one of the engineering wonders of the nation. A British visitor named David McCrae, wrote with astonishment: *"Great blocks of masonry. . . . have been lifted from four to fourteen feet. The Briggs House, a gigantic hotel, five stories high, solid masonry, weighing 22,000 tons, was raised four and a half feet, and new foundations built below. The people were in it all the time, coming and going, eating and sleeping—the whole business of the hotel proceeding without interruption. . . ."*
McCrae thought the moving of houses even more bizarre: *"Never a day passed that I did not meet one or more houses shifting their quarters. One day I met nine. Going out Great Madison Street in the horse-cars, we had to stop twice to let houses get across."*

For the first time since the city was incorporated, Chicago had a working sewer system. More than that, Chicagoans had demonstrated an ability to seek out the best possible solutions to their pollution problems. Not at all reluctant to pay the price necessary for sanitary conditions, they indebted the city through bond issues and indebted themselves through tax assessments to finance improvement. This "I Will" spirit was to serve the city well in the years ahead.

3. Lithograph of Lake Street, 1869
Businesses moved upstairs and pedestrians had a difficult time climbing ladders up and down to sidewalks of uneven height as work progressed at an uneven pace. This drawing of an entire block between LaSalle and Clark streets on Lake Street shows a happy and affluent citizenry disregarding the inconvenience, since raising the grade signaled the coming of a working sewer system.

All photographs are on file with the Chicago Historical Society

3

The Intercepting Sewer System

The second step in the gigantic sanitation program involved sealing off all wastes from Lake Michigan. This was accomplished by constructing huge intercepting sewers 6 to 27 feet in diameter. On the north side these converge at the Lawrence Avenue pumping station. On the south side they meet at the Racine Avenue pumping station. The intercepting sewers were linked to the city's system of collecting sewers. By 1907, the basic system had been completed and Chicago became the first Great Lakes city to stop using the lakes as a receptor of its normal domestic sewage.

When the Sanitary District grew by later annexations, other intercepting sewers were built along the lake shore. The North Shore Channel was built to bring fresh water from the lake at Wilmette into the North Branch of the river. The dilution system was completed with construction of the Calumet-Sag Channel which reversed the flow of the Calumet River and discharged its waters into the Sanitary and Ship Canal just above Lemont, Illinois. The total cost of the construction of the canals, sewers, locks, pumping stations and associated works of this drainage system was $125,091,977.

4. Concrete Sewer Construction, 1958
The 21.5 by 19.35 concrete sewer in 49th Street is shown preparing the arch pour on the curve at Kilbourn Avenue on the Leamington 1-A project.

5. By-Pass Channel, 1956
This man is standing in the by-pass channel connecting an 8-foot sewer to an 11-foot sewer at Lockwood and Bloomingdale avenues.

6. Sewer Construction, 1962
Placing reinforced steel for monolithic concrete sewer section thirty feet below ground surface, at 115th and Longwood.

All photographs are on file with the Chicago Historical Society

4

6

Sewage Reclamation

With the advances in chemical treatment, sewage treatment plants can recycle raw sewage producing a stable, odorless, organic fertilizer. Sewage that once decimated land is today used to reclaim unproductive farming areas.

Realizing that sanitation is a problem which extends beyond city limits, the Metropolitan Sanitary District of Greater Chicago, first called the Chicago Sanitary District, was established in 1889. The District was to provide for the collection and disposal of sewage from Chicago and the surrounding area and to prevent flooding by polluted water. Today the District serves an area of 860 square miles, serving 5,500,000 persons and an industrial waste load equivalent to 4,500,000 persons.

Chicago's sewage is processed in the largest treatment plant in the world. The District processes 1.3 billion gallons of wastes daily, removing 1,000 tons of dry organic solids per day. To date, funds in excess of $600 million in capital improvements have been invested.

Treatment plants constructed around 1930 produced an effluent water discharge which was 90% pure. This, however, is not adequate to permit return of the effluent to waterways used for recreational purposes. As a result of continued research, more sophisticated methods have been devised so that the effluent discharging from the plant is even clearer than most of the waterways and streams into which it is discharged. By the present program, this effluent will be 99+% pure by 1977.

Sustaining the environment is a never ending task. The fact that every other day four barges are loaded with 9,000 tons of liquid fertilizer, where once this sewage fouled the environment, is a tribute to the engineers and scientists who developed these procedures and offers encouragement to environmentalists who are today gravely concerned with urban ecology. Yet, in a broader sense, local pollution can only be abated by community participation, acting in all areas of conservation protecting not only our own but the environment of future generations.

7. Treatment Plant, 1972
The West-Southwest treatment plant at Stickney, Illinois, is the largest such plant in the world, treating approximately one billion gallons of sewage per day. Barges take liquid fertilizer 200 miles down river for a land reclamation project in Fulton County, site of Edgar Lee Master's Spoon River Anthology. Years of strip mining have left the land in poor condition. Fulton County is located 180 miles southwest of Chicago.

All photographs are on file with the Chicago Historical Society

7

The Underflow System

A bold new plan for flood and pollution control is underway in Chicago. This concept consists of boring large storage chambers and vaults several hundred feet underground in the solid bedrock which supports Chicago. During times of flood, polluted water is to be stored and later pumped out when weather conditions permit.

The complete Underflow System, as it is called, consists of a system of large tunnels, storage reservoirs, pumping and treatment facilities which will provide both flood control and pollution abatement. This engineering innovation provides a creative and practical solution of considerable national significance.

Since the end of World War II, metropolitan Chicago has undergone extensive urban development. Each new rooftop or paved parking lot caused a tremendous increase in the amount of impervious surface areas, resulting in a large runoff of storm water and more rapid peaking in the existing combined sanitary and storm water sewer systems. When the capacity of these combined sewers is exceeded during heavy storm periods, water backs up in basements and underpasses. The construction of auxiliary outlet sewers over the past two decades has been progressively increased, reducing this flooding; however, the great quantities of storm water runoff exceeds at frequent intervals the capacity of the sanitary intercepting sewers and sewage treatment plant facilities of the Metropolitan Sanitary District. This excess flow of mixed storm water and sewage overflows and carries polluted water to the surface waterway system. As the city has grown and runoff quantities became greater, it has become necessary at increased frequencies during heavy storm periods to open the gates and release polluted river water to Lake Michigan at the Wilmette Controlling Works, the mouth of the Chicago River and through the Calumet River.

During recent years, various schemes were advanced for dealing with the storm-runoff overflow problem. Studies were made on the feasibility of temporary detention of the combined flows during storm periods in deep underground tunnels mined in limestone bedrock. In 1967, the first contract for a five-mile section of deep tunnel design, called the Underflow System, was started under Lawrence Avenue by the City of Chicago. Two additional Underflow systems have been placed under contract by the Metropolitan Sanitary District, one along 47th street in LaGrange and the other under Crawford Avenue, north of the Calumet Sag Channel.

A technological innovation, known as mole tunneling, has been developed for use in this demonstration project. Mole tunneling, both practical and economical, is saving the City about 20% in construction costs and will reduce construction time, when compared with traditional sewer construction, from a five year to a three year period. In addition, this concept does not interrupt the function of conventional sewers and will not disrupt the community with unnecessary noise, such as normally experienced with conventional blasting methods.

These underflow systems store the polluted flow during small and medium rainfalls, reducing the frequency of overflow to the waterways to four or five instances per year instead of the normal 60 to 70 per year for the existing systems. The stored polluted water is pumped to the intercepting sewers and treatment facilities in the post-storm period before being released to the river. During heavy rainfall periods, when the volume of runoff exceeds the tunnel storage volume, the Underflow system will provide large conveyance capacity to reduce underpass and basement flooding. While the three Underflow systems under construction will provide pollution and flooding reduction for their local service areas, they are merely pilot projects for the metropolitan-wide flood and pollution control problems.

One of the activities of the study has been the collection of data for the approximately 5,000 miles of combined sewers, the determination of land use and population, both present and projected, for each drainage area, the collection of rainfall data on some twenty gauges for twenty years of record the investigation of 680 outfalls the assembling of treatment plant and pumping station records; and the collection of rivers, canals, and stream data. All of these data are on punch cards for use in more than a dozen separate computer programs.

A computer program takes hourly rainfall records and simulates the continuous runoff and sanitary flows throughout the year, along with the continuous pollution loads being discharged from each drainage area. Other computer models analyze in detail separate storm periods, flow to treatment plants with storage facilities, distribution of flows with various alternative system layouts of conveyance tunnels and storage facilities. The computer also routes the flows through the rivers and canal system to determine the magnitude of flood flows and the pollution impact on the waterways with each of the alternative plans.

8. Hard Rock Boring Machine
The cutting face of the forward section of the revolutionary hard rock boring machine, nicknamed "Mole," is shown on surface before being lowered into tunnel site. Machine is also used for vertical drilling of drop shafts.

9. Underflow, 1972
In 1972, the Underflow System neared completion in the first phase of development after five years of deep rock tunneling under Lawrence Avenue near the north branch of the Chicago River. The tunnel runs for five miles through niagaran limestone at a depth of 250 feet and is capable of storing four million cubic feet of water for a 3,620 acre drainage area. The second phase will include the drilling of ten drop shafts scheduled for completion in 1973. A similar project, the Mt. Greenwood Underflow is also nearing completion. Two sites are under construction: at 105th Street between Crawford and Spaulding and at 116th Street between Crawford and St. Louis.
When completed the Chicago Underflow system will store runoff water during heavy precipitation in an effort to eliminate flooding through a system of 120 miles of conveyance tunnels covering a 375 square mile area serving Chicago and 56 suburbs. This unique flood storage concept will give Chicago the only system of its kind, ending 150 years of flood and pollution problems.

10. Hard Rock Tunneling
Looking into the Underflow tunnel the circumferential scoring paths of the Mole are visible radiating from the left. To the right is the finely bored conduit wall. The smoothness of conduit walls bored by Mole eliminated the need for lining the tunnels with concrete, which was necessary with the older, conventional drilling and blasting tunneling method.

All photographs are on file with the Chicago Historical Society

When made operational, this project will demonstrate the practicality and economy of large-scale underground facilities for temporary storage of excess volumes of combined sewage produced during periods of rainfall. No city in the nation is currently using such a system, which will be applicable to all highly developed urban areas where space and surface storage are uneconomical.

The magnitude of this project will rival the engineering feat at the turn of the century of reversing the flow of the river away from the lake. Within the next decade, the rivers and canals may once again become recreational areas with fishing, boating and even swimming in certain reaches.

8

9

10

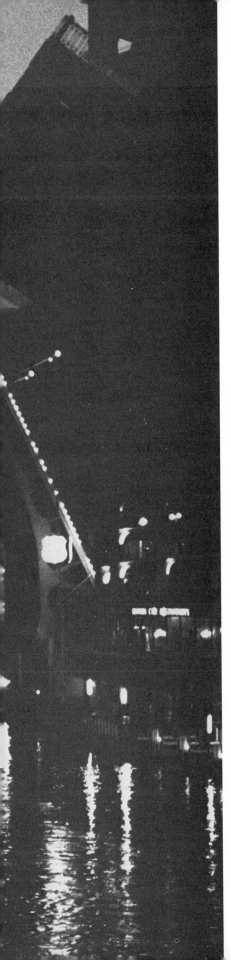

Bridges

Bridges at Dawn 1973
*An exhilarating sight rewards the early
riser as the Chicago bridges open for river
traffic before sunrise. Chicago's bridges,
like the fountains of Rome, are world
famous for beauty and service,
representing more than a century of
engineering achievement.*

Early Bridges

The first bridge was built across the North Branch in the winter of 1831-32 by a private tavern and store keeper to encourage customers from the west bank. A year later, a bridge was built across the South Branch at a cost of $486.20, $200 of which was contributed by the Potawatami Indians. The labor was done by soldiers from Fort Dearborn. According to the later recollection of four residents of the 1830's, both bridges reached from log abutments in shallow water near the banks and across two bents, each of four heavy logs, resting on the bottom in deeper water. Stringers of split logs formed the 10 to 12-foot wide bridge decks, about 6 feet above low water. Railings were added a few years later. Apparently the supporting logs rotted so badly that in 1837 heavy logs were lashed to the bridges to make them float, but then they could serve only as foot bridges.

The first movable bridge, the Dearborn Street Bridge built in 1834, was a primitive castle drawbridge type constructed of wood. It had two movable leaves which were lifted with chains to provide a sixty-foot opening for the passage of marine traffic. At each end of the movable sections was a framework tower of upright timbers connected at the top. These structures resembled gallows. The "gallows" appearance of the bridge towers was said to have startled visitors passing the site, particularly at night. The bridge was unreliable and earned the displeasure of pedestrians, wagon drivers and ship skippers alike. The blows of passing ships necessitated repairs in 1835 and again in 1837. In July of 1839, the bridge was ordered dismantled.

Seeking to cut off agricultural commerce on the North Side and fearful that the Council might rescind its action, Southsiders armed with axes gathered in the dark the following morning on the south bank. By dawn, the Dearborn Street Bridge was nothing more than a debris of shattered timbers.

Construction of another movable bridge took place in 1840. This was a pontoon swing bridge at Clark Street. Like so many major public works endeavors, it was hotly contested, as indicated in this story published in the *Chicago Times*.

1. First Movable Bridge, 1834-1839
The wooden drawbridge at Dearborn Street firmly connected both North and South banks for the first time. Once the draw mechanism jammed and traffic piled up for two days and nights. The bridge was torn down by a group of angry citizens in 1839.

2. West Foster Avenue Bridge, September, 1914
This pastoral scene, looking east on Foster Avenue, has long since disappeared, although the sturdy bridge is still in use.

All photographs are on file with the Chicago Historical Society

1

"Every night there came up out of the south a great fleet of prairie schooners that anchored on the Reservation. It often numbered five hundred, and came laden with wheat and corn and all sorts of produce. All the warehouses were in that day built on the north bank of the river. The South Side opposed the Clark Street Bridge, in order that their prairie schooners might not reach those warehouses, and thus be compelled to trade on the south bank."

The Clark Street Bridge, the first publicly financed public works project of note, was built at a cost of $3,000. It was a simple structure anchored to each bank, first by ropes which floated and often obstructed the passage of boats, then by chains fitted to windlasses, one stationed east and the other west of the floating bridge on opposite banks. To accommodate marine traffic, the bridge was swung open by cranking one windlass and slacking off on the other. To close, the procedure was reversed.

A pontoon bridge of similar type was built in 1841 at Wells Street. Six years later it was replaced by another floating bridge at a cost of $3,200. Its total length was 202 feet, with the draw section floating on boiler-iron drums. Stringers supported the deck which was 100 feet long from the pivot to the opening point, making a marine passageway 81 feet wide. The bridge had two tracks for teams and a sidewalk on either side for pedestrians.

That same year (1847) two more floating bridges of modified design were installed at Madison and Randolph streets across the South Branch. These may be described as "semi-floating" draw bridges, which indicates that the pivot ends were supported on solid abutments. Both were equipped with self-regulating aprons that rested on the roadway to maintain a desirable alignment despite variations in water height and bridge loading. They also had two lanes for teams and walks on both sides. The Madison bridge cost $3,200 and the Randolph structure was $5,000, probably because of a more elaborate and costly system of "self-adjusting aprons" at the land ends.

2

Flood Disaster

The snows of the winter of 1848-49 were exceptionally heavy. On March 12, 1849, a disastrous flood swept Chicago, wrecking the ships at anchor, damaging the wharves and destroying all of the bridges.

The city acted to repair the enormous damage wrought by the flood. As plans were being drawn up by bridge engineers, the Council sought funds through subscriptions of those owning property in the vicinity of sites designated for new passageways across the river. Meanwhile, three ferries and two jury structures were employed to cross the waterway. One of these was a canal boat at Randolph Street, the other a schooner at Clark, both moored athwart the river connecting the opposite banks.

The state of the art of bridge engineering was still primitive in 1849, in marked contrast to the technological excellence to be achieved by later designers of Chicago's famed movable bridges. Much was learned by repeated trial and error in earlier structures. Although the basic approach was not much improved by 1849, experience enabled designers to move swiftly and avoid previous errors as they worked to replace the structures wrecked by the flood.

In June, 1849, the Madison Street bridge was rebuilt and opened to travel. About two weeks later (July 3rd), teams passed over the new Clark Street structure, constructed in six weeks, a record time that subsequently has not been surpassed. The Wells and Kinzie bridges were completed in September. The Randolph Bridge was replaced about the same time as was a new one at Van Buren. By 1853, there were new pontoon bridges at Lake Street and Chicago Avenue in addition to a railroad bridge at North Water Street.

The advances in bridge design and construction since 1849 were visibly demonstrated on February 9, 1857, when Chicago experienced still another flood. Its ravages were general along the Rock River, including the disruption of the Galena and Chicago railway operations. On the North Branch of the river an immense gorge of ice formed at the Chicago Avenue Bridge. This mass broke up, subsequent to heavy rains, and the blocks of ice passed into the lake causing only relatively minor damage.

3a. Flood of 1849, Daguerreotype
The disaster of 1849 wrecked shipping and destroyed all the bridges. Fort Dearborn and the lighthouse are shown at the right; Lake Michigan in background then covered land on which the Chicago lake shore high rise development now stands.

3b. Aerial View, 1973
A recent view of the same site shows the curve in the river where once Fort Dearborn stood, a site now obscured with tall buildings. The locks at the river entrance were built under court order to restrict the water flow from the lake after the flow of the river was reversed. The Central Water Filtration Plant is visible in the upper left hand corner of the photograph.

All photographs are on file with the Chicago Historical Society

3a

3b

Swing (Pivot) Bridges

The shippers and marine interests objected to the impediment to river traffic caused by the bridge obstructions. Structural engineers were commissioned to study the problem of developing improved movable bridges.

This effort brought about the design of the so-called swing bridge. This type of bridge was supported on a pier in mid-stream and rotated on a horizontal plane. When open, the structure lay parallel to the center line of the stream and afforded a passage for vessels on each side of the pier, which had a diameter equal to the width of the bridge.

The first of this type was a crude wooden structure called a "pivot bridge." It was erected at Clark Street in 1854, at a cost of $12,000. The following year both ends of the bridge sagged, because the arched top chords of the timber superstructure gave way. The damage was repaired by bolting on heavy iron plates to reinforce the timber.

That year, officials moved to alleviate the chaos in the street traffic using the bridges, which frequently backed up for blocks when the structures were opened. An ordinance was passed giving precedence to traffic running with the bridge, then to that turning right into the traffic pattern, and lastly to carriages and wagons making a left-hand turn to approach the bridge.

Before 1856, Chicago's bridges were built mostly at the expense of citizens whose property values would be enhanced by such improvements. That year, it was proposed to build a swing bridge at Madison Street solely with municipal funds. In spite of vigorous protest, the project was publicly financed for $30,000 and completed the following year. It was the first Chicago bridge with masonry foundation.

During the same year, the old pontoon bridge at Randolph was removed and a new swing structure substituted at a cost of $20,811. Also in 1856, the Wells Street Bridge was built and at the time was the longest draw bridge in the West, 190 feet in length and eighteen feet above the water.

In June, 1856, the City contracted to design and build an iron swing bridge across the river at Rush Street at a cost of $48,000 with $18,000 to be paid with public funds and $30,000

4. North Clark Street Bridge, 1868
Early swing-bridge constructed chiefly of timber with some iron tie-rods. The bascule bridge which presently stands at Clark Street was opened July 10, 1929. A listing of Chicago's movable bridges together with opening dates is presented in the appendix.

5. Swing Bridge, 1873
Chicago's successful resurgence following the Fire of 1871 is evident from this river scene taken less than two years after the Fire. The bridge in the foreground is at State Street.

6. Bridge at State Street, April 1949
The Bataan-Corregidor Memorial Bridge, was dedicated May 28, 1949, with General Douglas MacArthur in attendance. The $3,000,000 span provides a 20 foot clearance over the river for a 103 foot width, and 16 1/2 feet for a 160 foot width which permits free passage of barges and tugs without opening the bridge and heavy street traffic. Construction of the bridge, which began when the State Street Subway was completed in 1941, was stopped in 1942 by order of the War Production Board and did not resume until 1947. This was the last bridge to use two bridge houses with two-man control operation. The heaviest of all the bascule bridges, this structure was designed to support, in addition to heavy commercial traffic, a continuous train of 50-ton street cars, as evidenced by the trolley arches visible in the construction photograph. The street cars were removed on February 18, 1957.

7. East 130th St. Bridge, 1941
A pontoon swing bridge. Note that one end of the movable span rests on a pontoon scow. Replaced by a modern fixed bridge in 1949. Photograph taken on April 11, 1941 looking north on the Calumet River.

8. West Adams Street Bridge, 1923
This three-truss swing bridge is shown in partly open position in a photograph taken just before demolition.

All photographs are on file with the Chicago Historical Society

divided between the railroads. When the bridge was completed in 1859, at a cost exceeding $50,000, it was the first iron bridge in the West.

During 1856-57, floating draw bridges were erected at Polk, Indiana and Erie streets, each costing $5,000.

4

5

7

6

8

97

Rush Street Bridge

Although the state of the art of bridge design was advancing, the trial and error approach remained the guiding principle. This was a costly method illustrated by reviewing the fate of successive structures at only one location, Rush Street, site of the first iron swing bridge built in 1859.

Before the swing bridge was built, Rush Street traffic was served by a floating bridge, hinged to one bank and opened and closed by means of ropes. In 1853, when the bridge was being pulled open with a number of laborers on the roadway deck, the structure careened and was swamped. A number of the laborers were drowned and the structure was wrecked. It was replaced by the iron swing bridge, which also met a disastrous end on November 3, 1863. At about five o'clock in the afternoon, with a hundred head of cattle, a horse and buggy and a horse-drawn wagon on the bridge roadway along with several people, a tugboat whistled about two blocks away. The events that followed were described in the *Chicago Tribune*: *". . . the cattle crowded to the south end of (the bridge). . . . the tender recklessly swung the bridge from the abutment. In an instant the north end of the bridge was elevated twenty feet in the air, there was a snapping of iron, a cracking and crashing of timbers, a shriek of horror from the bystanders, and the bridge, breaking in two across the center pier, fell with all its burden of people, cattle and vehicles splash into the river. . . ."*

A young girl was killed. Two-thirds of the cattle were lost. The first iron swing bridge in the West was totally destroyed.

The bridge was replaced by another iron swing bridge in 1864, and this one too was destined to be the scene of another costly accident. On the morning of November 23, a lumber-laden schooner was being towed westward up the river by a steam tug. From the opposite direction, a steam barge was leaving harbor. For some unaccountable reason, all three vessels chose to pass the opened bridge on the same (south) side of the center pier. The resulting collision drove the schooner's jib boom into the bridge at about the middle. Both ends of the structure slowly sagged onto the "protective" piling, which prevented the broken structure from

9. **First Iron Bridge at Rush Street,** 1856

10. **Rush Street Bridge,** 1863
The destruction of the first Rush Street Bridge.

11. **Refurbished Rush Street Bridge,** 1900

All photographs are on file with the Chicago Historical Society

10

11

dropping into the river. The damage was repaired within two weeks and survived without further incident until 1921, when construction of the adjacent Michigan Avenue Bridge caused settling of the Rush Street abutments, and the venerable structure finally was demolished and not replaced.

12

12 Rush Street Ruins, October 10, 1871
The wheels and circular track once used to swing the bridge are all that remain of the Rush Street Bridge. The Fire, which began on the West Side just after 9pm, consumed the Loop area and City Hall about two hours later and jumped the river around midnight. The Rush Street bridge shown here did not burn until about 7am the following morning.

All photographs are on file with the Chicago Historical Society

Destruction by Fire

Chicago was in a period of dynamic growth. In 1871, more than 12,000 ships arrived at the Port of Chicago and cleared for other ports. Railroad construction was pushing forward at a rate which by 1872, gave Chicago a claim to the title of railroad capital of the world.

In time the comparatively small sailing vessels gave way to the large craft propelled by steam. These steamers were wide of beam and demanded more and more width of channel if they were to ply the river. It soon became evident that Chicago's old swing bridge design, with a center pier obstructing the channel, would no longer do. Navigation interest demanded a clear, unobstructed river and at the same time land traffic demanded wide bridges that could be opened and closed quickly. An entirely new type of bridge was needed.

The great fire of 1871 wiped out the whole central portion of the city of Chicago and destroyed the bridges across the main branch at Rush, State, Clark, and Wells streets, across the North Branch at Chicago Avenue, and across the South Branch at Adams, Van Buren, and Polk streets.

The remarkable spirit and energy of the people of Chicago were shown in the speed with which crossings were replaced. Contracts were at once entered into to rebuild the bridges destroyed, and by the summer of 1872 they were practically all replaced by swing bridges but of a larger and more substantial construction.

Jack-Knife and Vertical Lift Designs

By 1890, when the city had 49 bridges, the problems encountered with swing bridges led engineers to consider different types of movable spans then being developed. Accordingly, a so-called "jack-knife" bridge was installed at Weed Street on the North Branch. This bridge had no center pier. The action of each half of the bridge resembled that of a loosely-hinged jackknife as it was lowered from the vertical position. In the raised position the hinged leaves folded against the supporting towers on each bank. The design, an ingenious contrivance, eliminated the objectionable center pier of the swing bridge, but the structure proved to be unreliable and costly to maintain owing to its many joints which were easily put out of order.

In 1892, so much objection was raised to the Canal Street swing bridge at a bend in the river that the two-year-old structure was ordered removed and replaced at a cost of $46,844 with a second jack-knife bridge which provided an 80-ft. draw. From the very beginning this too was troublesome due to light construction.

That same year it became necessary to replace the swing bridge at South Halsted Street. In its place the City introduced another type of movable bridge, the so-called vertical lift bridge. This structure operated like a giant elevator in which a steel span 130-feet-long and 58-feet-wide, weighing 280 tons, was raised vertically between two steel towers on the opposite banks to a height of 155 feet above the river to permit vessels to pass beneath it. The lift span was suspended from wire ropes passing up over large grooved wheels at the tower tops and down again to large counter weights of cast iron. Its cost was $242,880 and it served traffic until 1932 but was not problem free.

13. Canal Street Bridge, 1893 - 1902
The folding-lift or "jack-knife" bridge shown here was built in 1893 and dismantled in 1902 owing to problems in maintenance; the site was without a bridge until 1948 when a Chicago-type bascule bridge was opened. Another folding-lift bridge was built at Weed Street in 1891 and removed in 1905; it has not been replaced. This innovative design was one of the steps which led eventually to the Chicago-type bascule design in use today.

14. South Halsted St. Bridge, November, 1920
A vertical lift bridge constructed in 1894 and replaced by a modern bascule span in 1934. Photograph looks northeast.

15. Torrence Avenue Bridge, May, 1956
One of the two remaining vertical lift bridges in Chicago, this one was opened in December of 1938. The other is at South Western Avenue, built during World War II and opened in December, 1942.

All photographs are on file with the Chicago Historical Society

13

14

15

Improved Swing Bridge Design

The later part of the 19th century saw intense engineering activity in bridge design, with significant advances in the evolution of Chicago's movable bridge design. The August 16, 1902, issue of *Popular Mechanics* called it a revolution:

"The method of spanning navigable streams is undergoing a revolution as a result of invention born of the complicated conditions existing along the Chicago River. . . . which was being almost blockaded in some parts by the building of center pier bridges, structures that were pivoted on a foundation with a large bridge protection pier that lay right midway the channel, dividing it at that point into two separate passageways. This river, a very busy stream, always crowded with vessels large and small, winds its way through the very heart of the western metropolis and constitutes the foundation and principal support of Chicago's commercial superway. It is the foremost harbor in point of tonnage, as well as in the number of arrivals and clearances of vessels, in America.

"Center pier bridges daily became more troublesome and traffic across them more congested. . . . Aside from the obstruction of the center piers, which often caused boats to become jammed between each other in the harbor, the bridges were cumbersome of operation. Several serious accidents made the conditions intolerable. Locomotives, cars, vehicles and men have plunged into the river while the bridges were open.

"Often the machinery would become inoperative, sometimes while the bridge lay open lengthwise the harbor, sometimes when closed and half open. Frequently, it was so as to block harbor traffic and frequently the street had to be closed until the bridge could be fixed. People were often caught on the bridge, when it would get out of order while open, and no matter how great their hurry they would have to wait until the machinery was repaired before they could get to shore."

Despite these frequent mishaps, swing bridge design had vastly improved. The testing procedures employed for the last iron swing bridge constructed at Rush Street demonstrated the progress in design and construction and also reflected considerable public confidence in the engineers who

16. Diversey Avenue Bridge, February, 1967
This old center-pier structure, built in 1896, is shown being demolished prior to the construction of the new fixed bridge.

All photographs are on file with the Chicago Historical Society

16

designed and constructed it.

This bridge was supported on a roller-bearing turntable on the center pier and was operated by a steam engine. Before being put into service, the structure was tested with the aid of hundreds of citizens who literally staked their lives and property on the soundness of the structure. At the appointed time, the north arm of the bridge was covered with 18 load teams and about 800 people, aggregating about 200 tons. The south arm of the bridge was unloaded and under this condition, the maximum deflection of the span was one-half inch. Then, the bridge was loaded from end to end with heavy teams and about 2,000 persons exerting a force of some 370 tons. This time the maximum deflection of the span was one-half inch. Finally, the Fire Department turned out with four engines and hose carriages which crossed the bridge at full gallop. The vibrations were described as moderate and when the bridge was swung open, no permanent deflections were found and the bridge turned as easily as before the test.

But, marine interests continued to complain about the center pier obstruction of the swing bridges. The land-oriented citizenry objected to the frequent and prolonged blockage of street traffic when the bridges were open. As early as 1873, proposals were advanced to limit the opening of bridges to certain hours; some even advocating that the bridges should be required to stay closed to river traffic all day and opened for shipping only at night. An ordinance passed in 1881 prohibited the opening of bridges for shipping during one hour in the morning and another hour in the early evening. Marine traffic, vital to the economics of the city, continued to take precedence at all other times.

17. Diversey Avenue Bridge, 1968
This three-span fixed-bridge replaced the center pier swing bridge built in 1896. The new bridge has a 50-foot roadway to relieve traffic congestion caused by the previous 19-foot roadway of the antiquated span. Since the late 1960s, with the increase in commercial shipping concentrating more in the Calumet area, there has been a decline in the north branch of the Chicago River for the passage of large ships requiring movable bridges. As a consequence, when bridges require replacement, fixed bridges can often replace movable ones at a substantial savings in cost and maintenance as illustrated by this case.

All photographs are on file with the Chicago Historical Society

17

The Rolling Lift Bridge

At Van Buren Street in 1894, a bridge was constructed with two movable leaves that came together at the center of the stream. Each leaf rolled up and down, like a huge rocking chair with cogs on its runners matching cogged rails on its abutment at the shore end. Called the rolling-lift bridge, it was the forerunner of today's bascule design. It was hailed as perhaps the final solution to Chicago's problems and was equipped with the latest electric and pneumatic appliances; air brakes and two 50-horsepower electric motors on each leaf. The rolling lift bascule bridge presented a dual advantage—as the leaves were raised through an angle of slightly less than 90 degrees they also rolled back away from the water to clear a wider channel for masted vessels.

Thus by 1895, the city had three types of bridges which did not obstruct the river when they were in an elevated position. The rolling lift bascule was the most promising type in the development of bridges capable of clearing Chicago's waterways for the passage of marine commerce.

18. Clark Street Bridge, 1929
Looking east from LaSalle Street, the Clark Street Bridge is shown under construction. The hoops at either end of the leaves were for streetcar lines and have since been removed. The center pier remains from the previous swing bridge, which remained in service until two months before completion of the new bascule structure. On April 30, just a few weeks before this picture was taken, a ship struck the old swing bridge which was dismantled during the first week of May, 1929. The new bascule bridge opened July 10, 1929.

19. North Halsted Street Bridge, August, 1941
Built in 1897, this Scherzer rolling lift bridge was removed in 1954 and replaced by a Chicago bascule in 1955. The large, white building reflecting in the river in the central portion of the picture is Montgomery Ward and Company. The railroad roundhouse in operation to the right was that of the Chicago, Milwaukee, St. Paul and Pacific Railroad. The roundhouse has since been torn down and the property is now owned by Zenith Radio. Photograph was taken looking southeast.

20. Van Buren Street Bridge, Nov. 8, 1949
A forerunner of the Chicago bascule design, the Scherzer rolling-lift bridge shown here at Van Buren, looking northeast, was replaced by a bascule bridge opened in December, 1956. The bridge in the background was the famous Metropolitan West Side Elevated Railway bridge used for rapid transit from 1895 until June 22, 1958, when service began on the Congress Expressway. Always used for electric trains, this bridge was the only four-track bridge in Chicago's history and also served the Chicago Aurora & Elgin Railway.

All photographs are on file with the Chicago Historical Society

18

20

The Chicago Bascule Bridge

In 1899, the City's bridge division in the Department of Public Works organized a team of engineers to make a critical analysis of all literature on movable bridges in the United States and Europe with the objective of determining the most suitable type for Chicago. The results were put in the form of a report which cited the pros and cons of existing systems. A type identified as a trunnion bascule, newly developed by the City engineers, was recommended.

Three designs were prepared by the division's staff, each differing somewhat in appearance, method of mounting, etc., but all involving the principle of revolving counter-balanced leaves on fixed trunnions (axles), rather than on the rims of huge wheels, the principle in the rolling lift bascule design. The word "bascule" comes from the French and simply means "teeter-totter," a device depending on weights at both ends of a beam supported on a fulcrum for its operation, a term familiar to almost every American child. The counter-balanced principle applied to bascule bridges, of course, is much more complicated than a simple "teeter-totter" and the analogy should not be taken too literally.

This is indicated in the annual report of 1900 which describes the trunnion bascule design as a fixed-center, double-leaf, counter-balanced bascule bridge. This means simply that the weight of the leaf extending over the river is equalized by weights at the shore end to facilitate its rotation. If all friction could be eliminated, a perfectly designed bascule bridge could be raised or lowered simply by a person walking along the roadway. To overcome the lack of perfect design, friction, structural deformations due to temperature, and wind stresses, electric motors are employed to actuate the mechanisms.

From 1903 to the present time every movable bridge built except the one at Torrence Avenue over the Calumet River has been of the trunnion bascule type. Torrence Avenue, built in 1936, due to its necessary very long skew span is a modern vertical lift bridge, one of the largest of its kind ever built.

Each bridge must be designed for its particular location, therefore, no two of Chicago's bascule bridges are exactly

21. East 95th Street Bridge, 1944
An early example of the trunnion bascule bridge, this was one of the first two built at the turn of the century. The circular superstructure has rows of small cross bars which are actually gear teeth which mesh with the concrete bedded gears under the bridge when the span is raised or lowered. Early bascule design, seen today at LaSalle and Clark St. echo this curving design in the superstructure although bascules function on a different principle, with a rigid superstructure. This bridge was replaced by a modern bascule in 1957, which can be seen in an aerial view of the Calumet River in the section on Waterways.

22. East 95th Street Bridge, 1958
The concentration of heavy industry and shipping along the Calumet River command reliable and efficient bridge operation. Each year the 95th Street bridge opens approximately 400 times while some bridges in this area approximate a figure twice this number. While bridges on the Chicago River are always closed during peak traffic hours for an hour each morning and evening with no shipping allowed during those times, bridges on the Calumet River are never closed to river traffic.

23. Twin Eisenhower Expressway Bridge, November 1955
Four great leaves, each weighing 3,515,000 pounds, rise and lower in unison as one bridge. One bridge carries west bound traffic, the other east bound. If one is closed for any reason, the other can be operated separately. Although the twin leaves appear several feet apart in the photograph, when lowered they are only inches apart and can be locked together to act as a single leaf. In the background, the Van Buren Street Bridge, nearing completion, can be seen and beyond that, the old Harrison Street Scherzer Bridge is seen in use before it was replaced by a modern bascule in 1960.

All photographs are on file with the Chicago Historical Society

21

22

23

alike. Also, since the construction of the first bascule bridge a great deal of thought has been given to improving not only the general appearance of the structures but also to the operation and maintenance characteristics.

The work of replacing the old center pier swing bridges with structures of the modern bascule type has proceeded until, at the present time, there are no City-owned swing bridges crossing the Chicago River and its branches.

In the construction of early bridges, principles of scientific design were unknown. A bridge was built and if it failed the next one was built of heavier material. Even in 1857, when the first swing bridges were constructed, methods of calculating stresses in trusses and bridge members had not been developed. But today the art has so far advanced that we are justified in calling bridge designing an exact science.

In the design of the modern bascule bridge the engineer knows in advance each force and action with which he must contend. Therefore, he can calculate mathematically the effect that those loads and forces will have upon each member of the structure.

Under the foundation he extends concrete piers down to the bedrock, thus making sure that there will be no uneven settlement. He provides for live load, the vehicular and pedestrian traffic; for dead load, vibration and impact as well as for ice and snow loads on the roadway when the bridge is in the closed position. When the bridge is in the open position, it must be able to resist a wind load up to 100 miles per hour from any direction. The designer must provide for all this by making foundations of sufficient weight and area, trunnions of sufficient diameter and machinery of such strength that the bridge can be opened or closed and held in any desired position regardless of extremes of wind, weather and temperature.

24. Michigan Avenue Bridge, March 1972
The newly widened Michigan Avenue Bridge, built in 1920, is shown looking south to the site where Fort Dearborn stood. Located in the cradle of Chicago, each of the four bridge houses contains a bas relief sculpture depicting Chicago's history. In the middle left of the picture the construction of the continuation of lower Wacker Drive and river plaza can be seen. The row of lights visible, just above, are those used to illuminate the Wrigley Building on the north bank of the river.

24

The Michigan Avenue Bridge

One of the most photographed bridges in the world, the Michigan Avenue Bridge is virtually a trademark of the Chicago scene. It is the first double-deck trunnion bascule carrying two levels of street traffic. Its construction in 1920, made possible the two-level development of Wacker Drive along the south bank of the Chicago River. The structure is a subject of continuing interest to students of movable bridge design everywhere.

This is a Chicago type trunnion bascule bridge providing an upper roadway for passenger vehicles and pedestrians, and a lower roadway for heavy commercial trucking and pedestrians. The foundations are carried on concrete piers, over 100 feet below water level. The bridge is composed of two leaves divisible along the center. When the leaf is in the open position each trunnion supports a load of over 800 tons. Each leaf is operated by four 100 horsepower electric motor, with two additional motors on stand-by.

The Michigan Avenue Bridge represents a tremendous mass of steel and masonry, but the designers so proportioned the material that the whole structure is perfectly balanced and operates like clockwork, quietly rearing its mass high in the air, or quickly moving back into the closed position at the will of the operator. It requires approximately one minute to open and can be closed as quickly.

25. Michigan Avenue Bridge, January 1973
Looking north toward the Wrigley Building, both levels of the Michigan Avenue Bridge are visible. This is the only bascule bridge in the world having both pedestrian and vehicular traffic on two levels. The Michigan Avenue Bridge was also the first split-span bridge where one-half of a span may be raised without raising the other half so that one lane of traffic can be opened while repairs take place on the other half. The Eisenhower Expressway bascule bridges offer the same advantage, but these are two separate bascule bridges, each having a different foundation and offset from each other.

25

26. Dearborn Street Bridge, September, 1964

The fourth Dearborn Street Bridge, opened in October 23, 1963, replaced an older double leaf rolling bascule built in 1907 and was removed in November, 1959. The new Dearborn Bridge is operated by a single bridge house shown in the photograph. Prior to War II, two bridge houses were required, one for each span, since the necessary electronic controls were not yet available for single-man operation. Most movable bridges built prior to the War also had four bridge houses, two being dummies to give a symmetric appearance valued at the time. First prize in the 1963–1964 national competition was awarded to the Dearborn Bridge by the American Institute of Steel Construction.

All photographs are on file with the Chicago Historical Society

The Evolutionary Process of Design

Chicago's modern movable bridges are the product of a long and continuing line of evolution, tracing back to the wooden drawbridges that spanned castle moats in feudal times. Chicago's first movable bridge at Dearborn Street was little more than a direct adaptation of that medieval design. Most of the evolutionary development has taken place in the last 100 years. Much if not most of design improvements, have evolved in Chicago, and the evolutionary process continues.

Today, the City of Chicago owns, operates and maintains more movable bridges than any other public agency in the world. Many of these existing structures are more than a half-century old; yet they continue to serve the purpose for which they were built, withstanding the daily pounding of modern traffic loads and corrosive action of snow-removal chemicals far beyond anything their designers could have imagined.

The bridges of Chicago are a familiar part of the city scene. As such, they are largely taken for granted by the city's 3.5 million citizens and 8 million residents of the surrounding metropolitan area. That they can be taken for granted testifies to the excellence of the original design and to the never-ending inspection, maintenance and repair program of the Bureau of Engineering.

Since 1900, 48 bridges of the "Chicago type" have been built over the city's waterways. Each successive bridge has been improved over its predecessors; nevertheless, the structural fundamentals are essentially the same and Chicago's movable bridges have become "textbook classics" for engineers.

The proud history of Chicago's bridges and bridge engineering is more than a local or regional story. They also have played an important role in time of national emergency. During World War II, the U.S. Navy commissioned the City of Chicago to alter low-clearance fixed bridges, originally designed to accomodate only barge traffic on the Sanitary and Ship Canal, in order to permit passage of sea-going warships. In a major engineering feat, the Western Avenue fixed bridge was converted to a vertical lift span and other structures were similarly altered, thus opening the way for the Great Lakes

27. 18th Street Bridge, July, 1968
The longest single leafed bascule bridge in the world, the 18th Street Bridge is also Chicago's newest, built in 1968.

All photographs are on file with the Chicago Historical Society

27

ship building resources to contribute directly in the national war effort.

As a result of this experience, some of the fixed bridges now being constructed over Chicago's waterways are "convertible," designed to be made movable if the need again arises.

It is safe to say that the city of Chicago owes its very existence to the great natural waterway connection between the Great Lakes and the Mississippi River basin—the Checaugou Portage. It is also true that Chicago could not have attained its present position as one of the great cities of the world without the great trunnion bascule bridges.

Viaducts

Traveling on bridges built above land, motorists seldom realize the beauty of design and extraordinary engineering which these viaducts contain. These graceful spans of concrete and steel sweep over railroad tracks, warehouses and truck freight terminals, but the visual pleasure of the sweeping span is often interrupted by all manner of tall elevators, warehouses, cranes and industrial equipment of every type. Only those underneath, the locomotive engineers, truckers and freight handlers are in a position to see a portion of the strength and elegance which the modern viaducts contain.

For the larger viaducts, the supporting caissons are sunk 80 feet below the Chicago datum to hard pan and in some cases all the way to bed rock. Below Chicago is a maze of underground utilities and other improvements which impede excavation. Subterranean Chicago is laced by sewers, electric lines, water mains, freight tunnels and variety of long abandoned foundations and other structural remnants reminding the excavator that someone has been there before. Since a cut in any utility can cause grave inconvenience to people above ground, each new excavation must be carefully planned in advance and, if necessary, relocation of existing utilities made without interrupting service. Building a viaduct over a land area is therefore much more than simply building an elevated roadway; it is a unique endeavor involving the hazards of subway construction with the sophistication of bridge design.

28. Aerial View of Bridges, 1972
The bridges of the main branch of the Chicago River are shown here with the North and South branches to the left and right. Wolf's Point, visible in the center foreground, is scheduled for extensive redevelopment. The large building in the center beside Wolf's Point is the Merchandise Mart which for years, before the construction of the Pentagon in Washington D.C., was the world's largest building with a floor area of four million square feet.

All photographs are on file with the Chicago Historical Society

29

29. The Halsted Viaduct, 1972

The Halsted Viaduct, finished in 1972, replaced a wooden viaduct built in 1884. The new viaduct consists of 487 feet of five-span, continuous haunched girder construction with a concrete decked bridge carrying two 24-foot-roadways, a 3-foot separating median and two 7-foot sidewalks. The total length is 1,118 feet including filled approaches. The concrete and steel viaduct spans the tracks of the Chicago and Northwestern and Milwaukee and Penn Central Railroads and is shown here crossing the Kennedy Expressway. The Halsted Viaduct is an outstanding example of engineering excellence of design and construction in a most difficult and obscure location, which promotes effective traffic circulation and mobility. The new Sears Tower, tallest building in the world, is shown under construction in the background.

30, 31. South Damen Avenue Viaduct

The ten block long viaduct stretches between 37th and 47th Street. The viaduct, 7,200 feet in length including improvements, contains two 25-foot roadways with a 3-foot separate concrete median.

All photographs are on file with the Chicago Historical Society

31

Subterranean Passages 7

Washington Street Tunnel, 1870
The first tunnel under the river was designed by City Engineer E. F. Chesbrough and built in 1868. Construction was delayed by numerous difficulties, some relating to the high water content, up to 58% in portions of the clay, others to an outcropping of hard pan. Drainage problems were never completely solved. The small building atop the tunnel contains a pump for removing surface drainage from the tunnel. The experience gained together with development of new techniques made possible the construction of the larger and more advanced LaSalle Street Tunnel.

River Tunnels

As a matter of necessity, Chicago developed world famed skill and technology in tunneling in order to build the water system. This new-found expertise in tunneling also played a role in improving land ways by providing an uninterrupted flow of vehicular traffic without impediment to marine commerce on the river. The first vehicular tunnel was constructed at Washington Street beneath the South Branch and completed in 1868. A second was commenced at LaSalle Street in 1869 and opened to the public on July 4, 1871. The plans for the Washington tunnel, which was 1605 feet long, were prepared by Chesbrough with the assistance of an architect named William Thomas. The 1890-foot-long LaSalle Street tunnel was designed by William Bryson. Later, this same tunneling capability was to be vastly extended for the construction of the subways, providing the basic research information on the nature of tunneling in soft clay which stands today as far and away the most comprehensive work on establishing standards of engineering guidelines in this valuable and specialized field.

1. The LaSalle Street Tunnel
Three tunnels in one, the LaSalle Street Tunnel contained separated lanes for vehicles and a third pedestrian tunnel. Costing $498,000 a total of 67,500 cubic yards of earth was removed. Gas lamps lit the passageway. During the Fire, when the bridges were swept away by flames, the tunnels provided an important escape route for the great crowds which surged through them. Opened on July 4th, 1871, the need for the tunnel was obviated by the opening of the LaSalle Street Bridge.

2–5. Drawings of Tunnels, 1877
Although photography was well advanced by 1877, drawing remained popular, particularly with the tourists who found the underground passages a continual source of interest. The title of these drawings are:
"Entrance to Roadway for Vehicles, Washington Street Tunnel"
"Going Through the Tunnel - The Roadway for Vehicles"
"Going Through the Tunnel - The Foot Passengers' Way"
"The River over the Washington Street Tunnel"

All photographs are on file with the Chicago Historical Society

Central Business District Tunnels

In 1901, private interests began developing an underground network of tunnels to be used for telephone cables. Later, in 1903, these interests were broadened to include the handling of packages and freight from Loop businesses to warehouses and delivery points.

By 1914, there were 62 miles of tunnels under the central business district on both sides of the river. At that time, the rolling stock consisted of 117 electrically powered locomotives and 3,000 cars which carried merchandise, coal and ashes throughout the business district.

Eventually, for reasons of obsolescence and economics, this intriguing underground railway was replaced by surface transportation, the motor truck. The system was acquired by the City. Today remnants of the tunnels are laced throughout subterranean Chicago.

6. Map of Freight Tunnel System
Chicago's Loop is laced with a network of freight tunnels which once delivered 650,000 tons of packaged freight and were also used to deliver coal and remove ash. Today the entrance to these tunnels has been sealed off from most buildings and new buildings do not include entrances to them. Water seepage is a continual problem.

7. Interior of Freight Tunnels, 1924
Forty feet below the intersection of Madison and State Street, these tunnels were still in use in 1924. In recent times the only visitors were inspectors from the Department of Public Works checking on the physical condition. Soon portions of the Central Area Transit Project will interrupt sections of these tunnels at intersections in the construction of the Distributor Subway.

All photographs are on file with the Chicago Historical Society

6

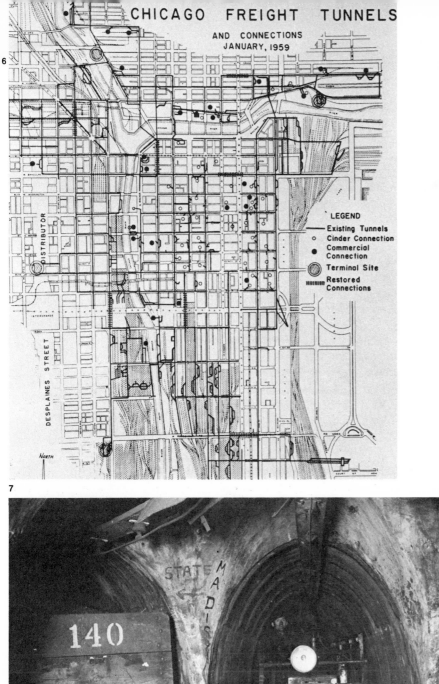

CHICAGO FREIGHT TUNNELS
AND CONNECTIONS
JANUARY, 1959

LEGEND
—— Existing Tunnels
○ Cinder Connection
● Commercial
   Connection
◍ Terminal Site
||||||| Restored
        Connections

7

Subterranean City

In inclement weather, the place to go in downtown Chicago is underground! For lunch, travel services, or a specialty retail shop, one of a host of City offices or access to major department stores, all can be found in this unusual city right underneath the original one.

Beginning in the mid 1960s, essentially as an extension of the subway system, the underground passages became arcades under major city and private buildings. The underground city had expanded to several acres with crowds of shoppers passing through on busy days. The success of this first subterranean effort has encouraged urban planners to extend the concept to broader range area. Currently, several more acres of subterranean living are on the drawing boards for Chicago's central business district.

This subterranean city has the important advantage of being climate controlled, a convenience to shoppers and stimulus to business particularly during the winter months. To encourage development of these underground passages, the Chicago City Council adopted special building ordinances giving "bonus provisions" when these pedestrian areas were included. Typically a 15 percent reduction in parking area is permitted. Other bonus provisions are given for connections with rapid transit facilities and for providing open space and plazas.

8, 9. Underground Shopping Area, June, 1972
Underground shopping and service areas for pedestrians adjacent to rapid transit facilities have been a successful joint city-private enterprise development. The scenes shown here are under the Brunswick Building. With the development of the new Central Area Transit Project and the Distributor Subway system, these underground facilities are to be extended. To encourage this development, a City ordinance provides a bonus provision of a ten percent reduction in required parking space for new construction if the building connects for each distinct passage connecting directly to rapid transit, and an additional fifteen percent reduction for a pedestrian circulation area.

All photographs are on file with the Chicago Historical Society

9

O'Hare Pedestrian Tunnels

The underground pedestrian tunnels at O'Hare International Airport link the terminal buildings with the airport hotel and multilevel parking garage. One day these tunnels will also connect with a people mover transit system.

There are six tunnels in all, two with moving sidewalks. Moving sidewalks are only practical where sufficiently long, obstruction free passage is available. Two of the O'Hare tunnels are 270 feet long which is adequate for a moving sidewalk; the necessity of fire doors at the terminal buildings, hotel and garage entrances prohibit these sidewalks from extending in those areas.

Moving sidewalks were invented in 1872 and were used for the first time at the World's Columbian Exposition in Chicago in 1893. Today these sidewalks, by law, can move no faster than 120 feet per minute, the same legal speed as set for escalators.

Each day, an average of 90,000 passengers arrive at O'Hare International Airport and 30,000 vehicles pass through on the access road in front of the terminal buildings. These tunnels help eliminate traffic congestion and provide a safe route for the handicapped. When completed in 1973, some 36,000 travelers are expected to use these tunnels daily including 600 handicapped. The first tunnels ready for use, those leading from the terminal building to the hotel and garage, were open in December, 1972. The Federal Aviation Administration allocated $3.2 million for these tunnels, the first such allocation of its kind in the nation.

10. Pedestrian Tunnels-December, 1972
Opening day, December 18, 1972, saw many travelers taking advantage of the newly opened pedestrian tunnels, even though finishing touches remained to be completed. The moving sidewalks are essential for the elderly and handicapped and a welcome addition for any luggage laden traveler.

11. Schematic Drawing of Pedestrian Tunnels
This map of the O'Hare International Airport pedestrian tunnels shows the relation of the tunnels to the terminal buildings, the O'Hare International Towers Hotel and the new parking garage. Eventually additional baggaging and ticketing areas will be placed in the basement level of the parking garage although at present, and for the near future, these facilities will remain in the main terminals containing the boarding and waiting areas.

All photographs are on file with the Chicago Historical Society

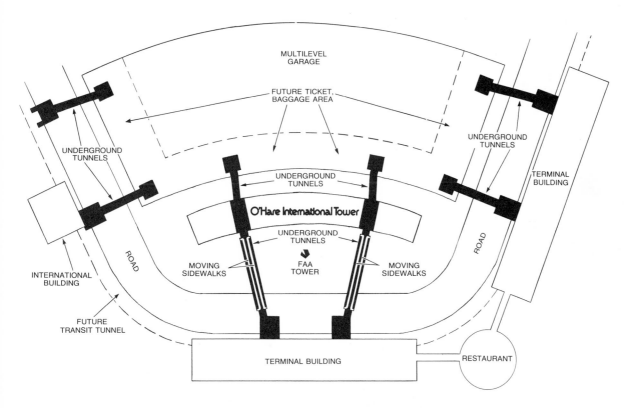

O'HARE INTERNATIONAL AIRPORT
Central Airport Complex Layout

Public Buildings 8

City Hall Interior, 1973
The beautiful architecture of an earlier age with extensive use of marble and mosaic work provides aesthetic pleasure for the generations of Chicagoans passing through these arcades. Public buildings such as this are designed to serve the ever changing needs of the city.

Early Buildings

As befitted a rugged, frontier trading post in the wilderness, Chicago's first public building was a log jail constructed in 1832. When Chicago became incorporated as a town in 1833, the City offices were located at Lake and Market streets. When the town became a city in 1837, the municipal services moved to the southeast corner of Lake and Clark streets where the Greyhound Bus station is now. Some of the City offices were in the basement of the one story brick court house erected in 1835, located at Randolph and Clark streets on the same site where the present City Hall and County Building stand.

In 1853, a two-story Court House and City Hall was built on the same site under the direction of Chicago's first important architect, John M. Van Osdel. A third story was added in 1858 together with a domed bell tower providing an uninterrupted view of the entire Chicago area. Van Osdel was later to gain fame and international recognition for his uniquely designed towering grain elevators and for the five-story iron front buildings as well as numerous homes of leading citizens. All were destroyed in the Fire of 1871.

1. First City Building, 1835
An artist's conception of the first court house shows the log jail at the rear and the basement used for some city functions. Names and responsibilities of early municipal professional staffs who served here are listed in the Appendix.

2. County-City Building, 1858
This domed structure survived until the Fire of 1871, although by that time additional wings had been added, some completed just before the Fire. The County-City buildings have always been located on the same site as today: the block defined by LaSalle, Randolph, Clark and Washington streets.

3. Temporary City Hall, 1871
The old water tank became a temporary City Hall following the Fire. Located at 209 South LaSalle street, this site was later leased to the University of Chicago for a period of 99 years. The Rookery Building, designed by architects Burnham and Root, was constructed in 1886; the now famous interior was the result of remodeling by Frank Lloyd Wright in 1905.

All photographs are on file with the Chicago Historical Society

THE FIRST COURT-HOUSE.

Reconstruction and Foundations

In the rapid reconstruction period following the Fire, the tendency was to build larger and taller structures to replace those destroyed. Serious problems ensued.

Before large buildings could be reliably constructed, particularly tall ones, it was necessary to develop foundations to carry their great weight over the filled, swampy soil. In response to the impetus given to architecture and construction by business entrepreneurs, many types of foundations were developed. Hugh Duncan in *Chicago's Famous Buildings* writes: *"Indeed, Chicago engineers were so advanced that the architects themselves were not able to keep up with them. Chicago grain elevators, which were built in the seventies on the banks of the River, used piling for foundations. Yet it was not until after 1890 that architects made common use of this type of foundation."*

In a monograph entitled *History of Building Foundations* in Chicago, by the Professor of Soils Mechanics at the University of Illinois, Ralph B. Peck, states that: *"The history of building foundations in Chicago between 1871, the year of the great fire, and 1915 epitomizes the development of foundation engineering throughout the world. Within less than half a century, and within the confines of the small area known as the Loop, the art of constructing building foundations grew to maturity by a process of trial, error, and correction. Seldom in any field of engineering has so much experience been concentrated in so little time and space."*

Many factors worked together to produce this unique experience. The most important, undoubtedly, was the presence of a deep bed of compressible clay which underlies the Loop, and without which no foundation problems would have arisen.

The phenomenal growth of the city after the Fire was accompanied by the continual construction of new and larger buildings. The progressive settlement of these structures on the soft clay bed became apparent, but the pace of new construction afforded little opportunity to observe the behavior of one structure before designing the next. Therefore, different architects and engineers diagnosed the

4. Post Fire City Hall, August, 1908
The spacious City Hall suffered from subsidence problems, typical of many large buildings built after the Fire. Built in 1885, the building is shown being wrecked in 1908.

5. Demolition, November, 1908
The arches of the County Building, occupying the eastern half of the block, are shown boarded up as demolition nears completion.

6. Caissons, January, 1909
Caisson work started while rubble was still being carted away. Caissons, 9.5 feet in diameter and 100.5 feet in depth, were hand dug.

7. Cornerstone Ceremonies, July 1909
At LaSalle and Washington, a crowd gathers while many position themselves in windows and balconies across the street.

All photographs are on file with the Chicago Historical Society

4

5

6

7

difficulties differently, and many variations in foundation practice were introduced. These variations constituted full scale experiments in the field of foundation engineering.

The final factor which made the Chicago foundation experience unique was that the period of phenomenal growth of the city was coincident with the transition from the traditional wall-bearing structure to the modern skeleton-frame building. Differential settlement became a matter of prime importance because it led to distortion of the masonry and of the structural framework and introduced supplementary stresses which were difficult to consider in the design. The quest for an unyielding foundation for the new skyscraper had an important influence on the history of Chicago foundations.

To understand the problems encountered, not only for building foundations but for supporting bridges and tunneling to supply water and build subways, it is necessary to comprehend the subsoil conditions in the Chicago area. As a result of raising the grade to about 15 feet above normal lake level (Chicago City Datum) with earth fill in the fifties and sixties and with rubble after the Great Fire of 1871, the top five to ten feet consists of miscellaneous compressible materials that are unsatisfactory for almost any kind of building construction with the exception of streets and sidewalks. Beneath the fill is commonly found a gray, lake-bottom silt of variable quality, normally consisting of sand that is loose and compressible but often sufficiently compact for light structures of one or two stories. This layer has a thickness of some five to ten feet. Approximately at the level of the lake is a crust of firm blue and yellow clay which acquired its stiffness by drying out ten thousand years ago when Lake Chicago ceased to exist. This layer is normally between five and ten feet thick and is an important feature as it serves to support the foundations of buildings three to six stories in height. In fact, most of the early skyscrapers were also founded upon it.

As the mass of structures increased, however, the pressure of their weights was transmitted to the thirty-foot-thick layer of wet compressible gray clay beneath the thin layer of desiccated clay. The result was the settlement of a number of buildings constructed in the 1880s and 1890s. Below the compressible clay is another thirty feet of tough to hard clay. Beneath this is a compact substance which the engineers call hardpan, a highly variable deposit, generally about 20 feet thick, but sometimes nonexistent. The lower portion of the hardpan generally consists of dense water-bearing sand, silt, or boulders. Bedrock (Niagaran limestone) is encountered between 80 to 120 feet below the surface. This now serves as the bearing material for most large post World War II structures.

The building practices employed during the reconstruction

8. City Hall Plaque, 1973
The foyer of the City Hall contains bronze plaques with historical background data such as this one shown here of the first Hall built after the Fire.

9. Nearly Completed, June, 1910
The familiar facade of today's City Hall is shown on the Randolph Street side to match up perfectly with the County Building exterior.

10. City Hall, 1911
A Parade of some of the nation's first motor vehicles, together with horse-drawn Hansom cabs, surround the new City Hall as viewed from LaSalle and Washington.

11. Interior of City Hall, 1969
While the exterior of City Hall has remained unchanged over the years, many improvements have taken place inside. During a major renovation project, 75 percent of the building from sub-basement to roof-top was renovated for greater efficiency and economy of operation. The Lobby is shown looking from LaSalle to Clark Street with the County portion of the building visible in the background.

All photographs are on file with the Chicago Historical Society

8

9

10

11

135

of the city after 1871 were approximately the same as those used during the two decades preceding the great fire. The height and weight of buildings, however, became greater which resulted in settlement.

One solution, advocated by Frederich Baumann in 1873, was to calculate the varying weights of the different components of a building and design a different foundation for each part so that the piers supporting the building rested on spread footings of varying dimensions. These spread footings were later to cause difficulty for engineers constructing subways and expressways since the building foundations sometimes exceeded the property lines spreading into the street right-of-way.

While public attention focused on the ever higher towers, engineers and architects were involved in an even more dramatic story taking place underground. The feverish race to find answers to the foundation problems was spurred by the differential settlement of six massive buildings in the Loop area. Buildings with their foundations sinking at different rates were threatened with eventual failure of their superstructural integrity. Three of these were public property: the Federal and County buildings and City Hall. As with the Federal Building, City Hall was supported by a thick concrete mat which supported the building's piers. The New York engineers who proposed the mat or "raft" foundation believed the concrete slab would tend to equally distribute the varying forces placed on the individual piers. This proved to be incorrect.

The County Building, adjoining City Hall, rested on wooden piles driven thirty to fifty feet below the city datum (lake level), but clearly not through the soft clay. By 1891 City Hall and the Federal Building each had a differential settling up to fourteen inches. The County Building sagged in places as much as eighteen inches. Repair was uneconomical and both were rebuilt.

In 1908 the City Hall was torn down at a cost of $323,975. On November 2, 1908, proposals were received for a new City Hall eventually costing $5 million to be erected within eighteen months. The new building was completed in 1911, adjacent to the new County Building which had been completed in 1907. The City Hall has proven durable, sitting in quiet dignity amidst the turmoil in the Loop, through war and peace, prosperity and depression. In 1969, a $6 million rennovation program was initiated to moderize the interior.

12

12. Street Scene, April, 1966
The LaSalle entrance to City Hall is always a busy scene. Here street planter boxes bring a landscaped quality to busy LaSalle Street, where an average of 30,000 pedestrians per day travel each block in the financial heart of the Midwest.

All photographs are on file with the Chicago Historical Society

McCormick Place and the Civic Center

Chicago's dynamic style of architecture stemming from the reconstruction period after the Fire, influenced design throughout the world. Until the period following World War II, this architectural style was primarily centered in private construction. The Civic Center and McCormick Place are important examples of contemporary design in public structures.

In Burnham's Plan, the Civic Center was to be placed west of the Loop at the location where the imposing expressway circle interchange now stands. Consequently, the Civic Center was built in the Loop's central section in close proximity to the City and County buildings. The Civic Center is 31 stories high, containing court rooms and offices. The exterior of the building is steel and glass, the steel being unpainted with a russet-brown appearance from natural oxidation requiring little maintenance. The exterior is designed to minimize the weathering effects of rain and snow.

The Civic Center building occupies only the northern half of the block. The rest of the block contains a street level plaza. "Chicago's Picasso", a Cubistic representation whose design was given to the City by Pablo Picasso, dominates the plaza area. The plaza also contains a fountain and pool, trees, landscaping and an eternal flame commemorating the war dead.

While the plaza is primarily intended for civic functions and events, the plaza also gives people a chance to get away from the traffic, rest a bit and enjoy the informal contact that has characterized street life of the past. As the city's buildings become taller and more imposing, architects have chosen to open up the spaces around the buildings by use of these small parks, plazas and malls breaking up the continuous lines of store fronts which has characterized the American Street. These plazas create a sense of light and spaciousness in contrast to the intimidating concrete environs of earlier business areas, establishing a new context for human contact and refreshment.

A different type of contemporary architecture is exemplified by the McCormick Place convention center. The first center,

named for the late Colonel Robert R. McCormick of the *Chicago Tribune* aroused considerable opposition since the location, on the lakefront in Burnham Park, disrupted the natural continuity of the lakeshore. Others felt it was too far from downtown hotels and restaurants. Containing 300,000 square feet, the building opened in 1960 and was an immediate financial success, serving somewhat to mute the critics. Fire gutted the entire installation in 1967.

The new McCormick Place, opened in 1969, offered substantial improvement in architectural design. The problem was to produce a building with greatly expanded floor space on the foundations of its predecessor. The solution was to introduce a two level exposition area in the north portion of the building, a 5,000 seat theater in the south portion with a broad pedestrian mall between the two. The roof is cantilevered on all four sides beyond the soaring wall of glass extending from main floor to roof. With immense horizontal dimensions, the building is an excellent example of elegance and strength in steel construction.

13. Civic Center Building, 1973
The 31-story Civic Center, built in 1964–1965, contains court rooms and offices. The Center stands across from the City Hall-County Building on the northern part of the block leaving a large open space for a public plaza. The massive 87-foot bays mark the building's simplicity and scale.

14a. Old McCormick Place, 1965
Destroyed by fire in January, 1967, the first McCormick Place utilized walls without windows; to lend interest to their vast expanse, the walls contained sculptured panels by Costantino Nivola but the relief was so low and rounded as to be seen best when floodlighted at night.

14b. New McCormick Place, 1971
Under control of the Metropolitan Fair and Expositon Authority, this building is the largest exposition hall in the United States. More than 1200 trade shows and conventions are held in Chicago annually, twice the number of the nearest rival, and brings over 1.5 million visitors to Chicago for commercial interests.

15a. Civic Center Plaza, 1973
The fountains of the plaza are dominated by the Picasso steel-plated statue. The scene of public gatherings and events, the plaza attracts pedestrians and offers tree shaded benches (out of view in this photograph). In the center background is the Standard Oil Building, the world's tallest marble-faced building, under construction.

15b. Eternal Flame, 1973
The eternal flame commemorating the war dead is shown protected by a decorative railing. This area is to the immediate right of Fig 15a. The Picasso statue can be seen in the background.

All photographs are on file with the Chicago Historical Society

13

139

Contemporary Municipal Buildings

The progressive approach to design of neighborhood facilities has produced a revolution of sorts in both the appearance and utilization of public buildings.

In times past, public structures were designed according to a uniform code; any fire station was identifiable blocks away. As was the custom of earlier times, the needs of the neighborhood communities were assumed to be nearly identical so that a uniform design code sufficed.

Today, no public facility is constructed without serious attention to the individual needs of the community it serves. Each design effort consists of an interdisciplinary team of engineers and architects working together with members of the professional disciplines of the proposed facility. Each structure is designed with a view of the needs of the people to be served, whether fire or police station, ward yard, health or service center or neighborhood library.

The unusual and successful Chicago neighborhood health centers are another example of the remarkable achievements of interdisciplinary team work. The goal of the project was to bring to the community the best possible medical and dental care, treating large numbers of people in the shortest possible time. Engineers and architects designed these unique facilities working together with teams of other professionals including physicians, dentists, sociologists, psychologists, medical technicians, para-professionals and health specialists. The preliminary studies showed that the health care needs varied distinctly from neighborhood to neighborhood so that each health center was designed in relation to those identified needs. The cluster clinic concept was developed in which all phases of diagnostic tests are performed within a cluster service area making optimum use of space and conserving time for both the patient and health center staff. Special dental operatories were grouped about para-professional service benches making it possible to treat a large number of patients in a given time period with smaller staffs than have had been possible previously. These centers also include other accommodations for patients such as child care centers.

The same progressive, interdisciplinary approach is evident

16. Lehigh Fire Station, 1970
Award-winning fire station at 6424 N. Lehigh features split-level design with concrete bas-relief by Bronislaw M. Bak. The split-level design eliminates the need for the hazardous brass slide-pole. The innovative design together with the 30-foot sculpture won two top honors including the Distinguished Buildings Scroll by the Chicago chapter of the American Institute of Architects and the Chicago Association of Commerce and Industry, and in addition, a landscaping award from the Chicago Beautiful Committee.

17. First Library
Chicago's first Public Library was built in an old water tank. The present building at Michigan and Randolph was one of the first major municipal structures built after the fire. The Library recently celebrated 100 years of service.

18. Chicago Fire Academy, 1961
Standing on the O'Leary property, the Chicago Fire Academy incorporates a sculpture entitled "Tongues of Flame" by Egon Weiner. This bronze work, over two stories high, reminds the viewer of the immense and sweeping proportions of the Great Fire of 1871.

All photographs are on file with the Chicago Historical Society

in all neighborhood centers today, whether police stations, fire stations, libraries, ward yards or service centers.

Another important change in the concept of municipal building development is the growing use of dual purpose projects. Today, excess land adjacent to public buildings, even though small and of odd shape, is utilized when possible for recreational purposes depending on the needs of the community. Swimming pools, small parks, atrium gardens, bus shelters and a variety of terraces and plazas are often incorporated in the total facility.

Effective and imaginative landscaping also furnishes an important element in unifying the buildings with the community. Every effort is made to provide exterior structural design which harmonizes with the surrounding community and identifies with the neighborhood imagery. Today's municipal buildings have become attractive neighborhood focal points, serving the people in a broad variety of capacities.

19. Brighton Park Branch Library, 1970
Sunken atrium reading area under a skylight is one of the innovative features, distinctive of this branch library. The Portage Park Branch Library has an identical design.

20. Woodlawn Health Center, 1972
A 14,500 square foot, one story structure at 6339 S. Woodlawn was the first of the seven new Health Centers to be completed in 1972. The architectural design used also for the North Kenwood West Town and Pilsen center, incorporates 28 rooms providing multi-phasic screening areas, medical specialities and emergency care facilities in addition to dental operatories, a radiology unit and a records center, administrative offices, a pharmacy and various supportive services. Landscaping is an important element of each new health center. Openspace parkways of trees and shrubs and benches are included in exterior designs.

21. Interior, Health Center, 1973
Public facilities receive heavy use requiring extensive care and maintenance as shown here on a typical day in the Uptown Health Center. The efficient utilization of space, furniture and equipment is evident in this photograph. Uptown Health Center at 845 West Wilson has 38,000 square feet of space serving 25,000 patients. The community of 150,000 is a blend of five ethnic groups; a representative of each group serves on the Health Center Advisory Board. Under-employment and low median income necessitate health care subsidizing. In Uptown, 45 percent of the population has an income of less than $6,000 per year. Patients pay according to a sliding scale rate which depends on income and financial status.

22. Drinking Fountain, 1973
All public buildings built today comply with the State of Illinois Handicapped Regulations. Drinking fountains 30 inches from the floor are an example of health center compliance. In this instance, small children also benefit from this specialized piece of equipment, taken in the Uptown Health Center.

All photographs are on file with the Chicago Historical Society

19

143

Refuse Disposal 9

The Northwest Incinerator, 1972
With the disappearance of landfill areas within the city, Chicago initiated vigorous leadership in developing high capacity incineration facilities which would not contribute to air pollution. The Northwest Incinerator, shown here, represents the culmination of these efforts. The Northwest Incinerator is the largest in the western hemisphere and so low in particulate emission that the site was used for establishing future standards in air pollution by the Federal Environmental Protection Agency.

First Incineration Facilities

On an average day, Chicagoans throw away about 5,000 tons of paper, plastics, garbage, metal and glass refuse. In addition, they discard nearly 300 tons of large appliances, tires, furniture and other items of bulky trash. This daily mountain of refuse is collected and disposed of by the Department of Streets and Sanitation. Private scavenger companies take care of an additional daily average of about 2,700 tons of assorted refuse.

The job of picking up and hauling away the things people no longer want is a monumental task, but it is only the first step in getting rid of it. The rest of the disposal process gets more complicated and requires the utmost care and technological resourcefulness to protect the environment from harmful side effects of air, water or ground pollution.

The first incinerator constructed was the Medill plant, located at 1633 West Medill Avenue. A small plant by today's standards, the facility has four furnaces with a capacity of 720 tons of refuse per day. Operation began in 1956.

The Calumet Incinerator Plant was the second of the originally planned four plants. Placed in operation in early 1959, the Calumet was at that time the largest built in the United States with six furnaces having a capability of almost 1200 tons of refuse for a 24 hour operation period. Installation of large subsidence and wet collector chambers removed particulate matter. The plant has five levels with enclosed tipping floor which allows all collection vehicles to unload inside the plant in order to eliminate the possibility of obnoxious odors and debris from emanating from the building. To further reduce dust from the dumping operation, water sprays are installed over the refuse pit. A special design ventilation system pulls odor laden air from above the storage pit for use as intake to the furnaces air supply system.

Chicago's third plant, the Southwest Incinerator, was put into service in December of 1962. The plant has a capacity of over 1200 tons and was the largest in this country when constructed. The burning section consists of four 300+ ton rotary kiln furnaces. The plant has a number of innovative features such as a wet bottom which helps move and remove

1. Medill Incineration Plant
Chicago's oldest incinerator, located at 1633 West Medill Avenue, was taken out of service in 1972 after 16 years of operation. Now used as a refuse transfer point while plans for a fifth incinerator are underway.

2. Calumet Incineration plant
Air pollution control equipment was installed at this older incinerator in 1972. Built in 1959, this incinerator has a capacity of 1200 tons per day, and now meets all federal, state and local air pollution standards.

3. Southwest Incineration Plant
The second largest incinerator in the western hemisphere, this facility also received air pollution control equipment in 1972, and when completed in 1973, will meet federal, state and local pure air standards.

All photographs are on file with the Chicago Historical Society

particulate matter from the mixing, subsidence and spray chambers of the furnace. An extensive water reclamation system was installed to keep water requirements to a minimum. Both the Calumet and the Southwest meet air pollution standards set by the City at that time as 0.2% parts per cubic foot. Today the Southwest is the second largest incinerator in the western hemisphere, second only to the newly constructed Northwest Incinerator.

The unequivocal success of these early incineration plants demonstrated beyond question the concept of economic refuse disposal through the use of advanced incineration techniques which could operate successfully in an urbanized environment without contributing to air, land or water pollution.

4. Cutaway of Southwest Incinerator
Forerunner of the massive Northwest Incinerator, the Southwest Incinerator incorporated the most advanced engineering of its time; the operations are illustrated in this cutaway drawing.

All photographs are on file with the Chicago Historical Society

4

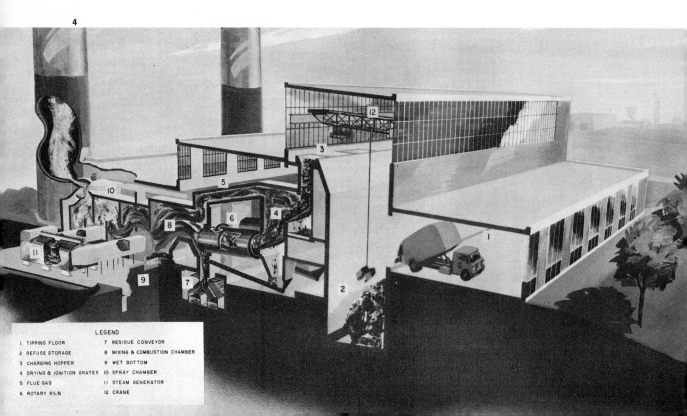

LEGEND

1	TIPPING FLOOR	7	RESIDUE CONVEYOR
2	REFUSE STORAGE	8	MIXING & COMBUSTION CHAMBER
3	CHARGING HOPPER	9	WET BOTTOM
4	DRYING & IGNITION GRATES	10	SPRAY CHAMBER
5	FLUE GAS	11	STEAM GENERATOR
6	ROTARY KILN	12	CRANE

Goose Island Bulk Refuse Grinding Station

Situated on an island in the Chicago River between Division Street and Chicago Avenue is a unique and remarkable device known as the Bulk Refuse Grinding Station. Furniture, refrigerators, carpets, tires and any object too large to be incinerated directly are shredded to a sufficiently small size as to be handled by incineration.

The plant handles approximately 50 tons of bulky trash per day. After grinding, the shredded material is trucked to a nearby incinerator and burned. Metal objects are separated out manually before shredding and sold to offset the cost of plant operation.

5. Goose Island
Centrally located in the north branch of the Chicago River is Goose Island, the site of the bulk grinding station. The 1865 Annual Public Works report mentions removal of the island by dredging 13,500 cubic yards of earth. However, during 1866-1868, the island was again reformed by the dredging of the north branch of the canal, forming the east side of today's Goose Island. Some say the original island was formed when in 1850 the Chicago Land Company dug for clay in the area and that the island was called Ogden Island after Mayor Ogden. The name Goose Island became popular when the area was settled by Irish Americans who raised gardens and geese.

5

6

7

8

9

6. Stearns Quarry, 1970
Now used as a land-fill site for the incinerator residue, Stearns Quarry will eventually become a park and recreational area. This photo shows the structured bedrock which forms the solid foundation for Chicago skyscrapers.

7. Building Exterior, 1969
The Bulk Refuse Grinding Station at Goose Island during final construction phase.

8, 9. Bulk Refuse - Before and After
Bed springs, metal containers, or refrigerators, whatever is unsuitable for incineration comes first to the bulk grinding facility where it is first shredded and then delivered for incineration.

All photographs are on file with the Chicago Historical Society

The Northwest Incinerator

Inspired engineering leadership can act to sustain the available urban environment in a number of ways. Civil engineering, particularly that related to Public Works, is in a pivotal position to broaden the scope of impact on community through the major, comprehensive projects which engineering directs.

The Northwest incinerator is an example of this concept. When design was initiated in the mid-1960's, concerns of ecology and the environment were much less prominent than today. Yet, realizing that major installations of this type endure for generations, and realizing that this particular incinerator would be the largest in the western hemisphere so that any undesirable effects would be magnified, the engineering design team endeavored to make use of every practical method to reduce stack emission and minimize air pollution.

When the Northwest Incinerator went into service in Spring of 1971, the results were astonishing: 97% of pollution particulates were removed. This emission is not only well under the .08 grams per cubic foot set as a goal by the Federal Environmental Protection Agency, but is also well below the new Illinois State emissions standards of .05 grams per cubic foot.

At its rated capacity of 1,600 tons per day, Chicago's Northwest Incinerator, which went on line in the Spring of 1971, is the largest of its kind in the western hemisphere and represents the next step in the evolution of the municipal incinerator; it is a sophisticated power plant which uses refuse as fuel. The low particulate emission is possible through use of electrostatic precipitators; the incinerator is under negative air pressure which keeps the odors confined within the buildings. In 1971 the Federal Environmental Protection Agency conducted a series of tests at the incinerator to establish design criteria for future incinerators constructed elsewhere in this country.

Chicago is now able to incinerate 100% of its present annual collection of 1.3 million tons of domestic refuse and consequently has phased out its landfills.

10. Northwest Incinerator Plant, 1972
The Northwest Incinerator, the largest in the western hemisphere, is also the most efficient in terms of reduced stack emission. 98% of particulate particles are removed through use of advanced design electrostatic precipitators. Because of the success of the air pollution control features of this facility, Federal Environmental Protection Agency conducted a series of tests at the incinerator to establish design criteria for future incinerators constructed elsewhere in the nation.

10

While the primary function of the incinerator is disposal of domestic refuse, it provides additional benefits as well, including water wall burning systems to make use of waste heat for production of steam to operate the plant, and for heating and cooling the buildings in the incinerator complex. Excess heat energy—about 40%—is available for sale to neighboring industries.

In addition, metals are separated out of the bulk refuse and from incinerator residue for sale to scrap dealers on contract. Each of the plant's four 400 ton per day burning units is equipped with a patented reverse-acting reciprocating stoker.

Controls for the plant are centralized in an air conditioned room in the main building. Closed-circuit television monitors provide constant surveillance of each furnace and supporting systems. The plant is equipped with the latest and most sophisticated equipment to obtain a high degree of automation thus reducing manual labor to a minimum. The plant operates 24 hours a day, 7 days a week with four shifts averaging 18 men each. This number is considerably less than for a comparable conventional incinerator.

The buildings are designed and landscaped to make the plant a welcome addition to a planned industrial park area.

The broad environmental accomplishments as shown by this incinerator represent not only the most creative of engineering efforts and superior technical capability, but also an early insight into the fundamental problems affecting the quality of life in the urban area and persuasive power at the initiation of the project to see that the essential features for environmental control are built into the project from inception. Achieving these broader scopes and goals requires determination and tenacity not only to accomplish the engineering technical feats required, but also to inform and communicate with the community as a whole, since successful conservation of our environment requires the support and cooperation of everyone.

11. Cutaway Drawing
The working components of the Northwest Incinerator are illustrated in this drawing which shows the dumping area and refuse pit at left, grate and electrostatic precipitators at right.

12. Pollution Control Equipment, 1971
These electrostatic precipitators effectively remove 98% of the stack emmission particles.

13. Interior View, 1971
Northwest Incinerator is shown in this interior view. Refuse from the storage bin is fed to the stokers through these hoppers and chutes.
The National Society of Professional Engineers named the Northwest Incinerator as One of the Ten Outstanding Engineering Achievements in the United States in 1971.

All photographs are on file with the Chicago Historical Society

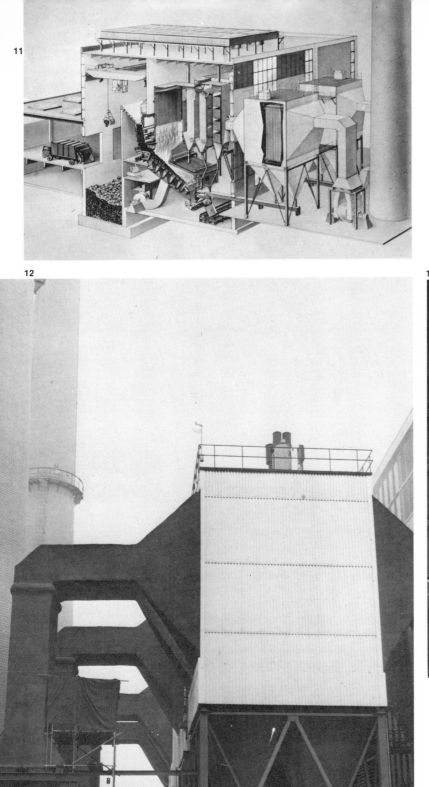

11

12

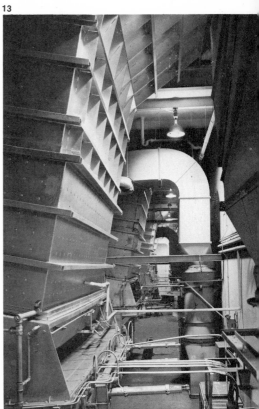

13

Expressways 10

Expressway Circle 1973
From the north, Chicago's Kennedy Expressway converges on the traffic circle delivering a daily outpouring of vehicles to either the Eisenhower Expressway to the west, or the Dan Ryan to the south. Chicago's growth as one of the great cities of the world stems from its unique and historical position as a transportation center. At the heart of the ground transportation system lies this distinctive interchange.

The Eisenhower Expressway

" . . . It is within reasonable financial possibility to develop a great avenue, extending from Michigan Avenue through the city and westward indefinitely. This would result in providing for all time to come a throughfare which would be to the city what the backbone is to the body. The selection of Congress Street for development into a broad cross avenue is urged."

From the *Plan of Chicago* developed in 1909 by Daniel H. Burnham and Edward H. Bennett, noted Chicago architects.

The "Backbone" of Chicago, the Eisenhower Expressway, was conceived by Burnham in 1909 and became a reality in 1956. Spanning the city from Grant Park downtown westward, the gleaming ribbon of freeway became an important factor in relieving traffic congestion and in stimulating commerce.

Demonstrating how expressways can strengthen mass transit, the Eisenhower incorporates rapid transit tracks in the median of the expressway. Strong guard rails along the inner side of the median insure separation of motor vehicles and transit lines.

Other features include giant $5,000,000 twin bascule bridges, so designed that when one bridge is inoperable due to maintenance, the other can be kept in service.

The most distinctive single feature is the massive circular interchange just west of the Loop. Here the Dan Ryan, Kennedy and Eisenhower Expressways merge in a series of expanding, concentric circular patterns. So distinctive is this interchange in providing a memorable landmark, that when the University of Illinois built a commuter campus nearby, it was named "Chicago Circle Campus", illustrative of the impact of the Eisenhower on Chicago.

1. **Expressway Map**
A schematic diagram of Chicago's expressway system shows the partially completed system; seven expressways funnel into the main stem of the Dan Ryan-Kennedy routes, with the entire radial pattern converging on the Loop. The concentric portion of the system, the Crosstown, has been designed. A table of expressway construction dates and mileage data is presented in the Appendix.

2. **Interchange, 1973**
Expressway passes through the Chicago Post Office into the interchange. The Post Office, built in 1932 left an opening for this expressway, which was not built until 33 years later, according to the Chicago Plan of 1910 which anticipated the need for the western highway. The Chicago Post Office is the largest mail transfer station in the world.

3. **"Congress" Expressway, 1956**
Called the "Congress" Expressway when this photograph was taken shortly after opening, Pulaski Road can be seen on the lower right.

4. **Chicago River Crossing, December, 1956**
The Eisenhower Expressway with the twin bascule bridges carries over the south branch of the Chicago River.

5. **Edens Expressway,**
Located in the suburban area northwest of Chicago, the Edens Expressway, completed in 1951, links with Chicago's Kennedy Expressway.

All photographs are on file with the Chicago Historical Society

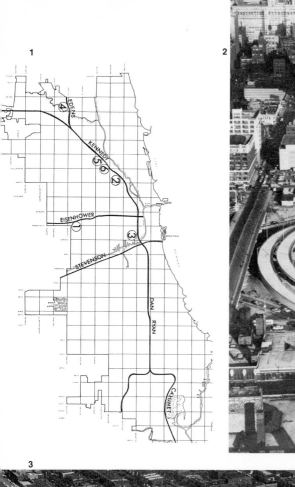

1

2

3

4

5

The Dan Ryan South Expressway

The Vincennes Trace, carved out by the wheels of the early settlers' wagons, connected the pioneer village of Chicago with Vincennes, Indiana. The "trace" followed earlier trails formed by moccasined feet of Indians.

The $300 million Dan Ryan South Expressway, opened to traffic in 1962, retraced this ancient thoroughfare with multiple lanes of reinforced concrete. In the center median strip, the extension of the electric rails of the Chicago Transit Authority provide rapid mass transportation facilities in high speed, air conditioned trains from 95th Street to the Loop in 20 minutes.

Another unique feature of this route is a continuous collector-distributor roadway constructed between 27th and 65th streets. In effect, this provides two separate sets of parallel express roadways with 14 lanes of traffic in this area: a pair of inner roadways for through traffic and a pair of outer roadways for more localized traffic. This design permits frequent points of access to and from the "local" expressway reducing the weaving and merging maneuvers of motorists and the potential of accidents.

Known as the South Route Expressway when the Comprehensive Superhighway System was originally adopted by the City Council in 1945, the route was renamed the Dan Ryan South Expressway in 1961 in memory of the late President of the Board of County Commissioners, Daniel Ryan, whose active interest and productive efforts stimulated the development and expansion of the transportation facilities in Cook County and the City of Chicago.

6. Dan Ryan, December, 1964
Looking north at 26th Street on the then "South" expressway.

7. Dan Ryan Elevated, 1969
Bird's-eye view of the elevated structure connecting the rapid transit service from the median of the Dan Ryan Expressway to the older, existing elevated structure leading to the Loop. The horizontal street near the bottom of the picture is Lake Street; the street near the center of the photograph intersecting Lake Street is 18th Street.

8. Dan Ryan, January, 1963
Snow covers the Dan Ryan as traffic moves smoothly through at about 59th Street.

9. Dan Ryan, 1969
Looking north from 39th Street.

All photographs are on file with the Chicago Historical Society

7

8

9

The Stevenson Expressway

Progressing from Lake Michigan, the Adlai E. Stevenson runs southwest, crossing the Dan Ryan. Passing as it does through a heavily built-up section of the city, the expressway is a massive complex of railroad grade separations, cross-street bridges and elevated and depressed highway sections.

Important in relieving congestion on other freeways and in stimulating industrial development in the southwest, the Stevenson Expressway when opened in 1966 represented completion of a major link in the Chicago transportation network.

10. Dan Ryan- Stevenson Expressways, 1969
Here the newly opened Dan Ryan passes over the Stevenson Expressway which is in the final stages of construction.

11. Dan Ryan- Stevenson Interchange, 1969
The Chicago River and Lake Michigan are in the background.

12. Stevenson Expressway, 1969
View at Ashland Avenue and the south branch of the Chicago River.

13. Stevenson Aerial View, 1973
Under cover of winter, the Stevenson Expressway travels through southwest Chicago along side the Chicago Sanitary and Ship Canal.

14. Stevenson Expressway, 1965
Landscaping is going on as construction nears completion. Beside the Chicago Sanitary and Ship Canal, at Summit, the expressway is shown in final completion stage under relocated Lawndale Avenue.

All photographs are on file with the Chicago Historical Society

10

11

12

13

14

The John Fitzgerald Kennedy Expressway

Penetrating the city to the northwest, the Kennedy stretches from the heart of Chicago, to the giant O'Hare airport. Originally called the Northwest when constructed in 1960, the expressway was renamed for the martyred President by action of the City Council on November 29, 1963.

As with the other Chicago Expressways, the Kennedy includes mass transit facilities on the median strip. In addition, the Kennedy incorporates unique transit stations within the air rights above the expressway. The beautiful architectural design of these stations, coupled with the creative multiple-use of expressway right-of-way, has won two national design awards. The rapid transit system was dedicated and placed in operation on January 30, 1970.

Another innovative design feature is the reversible lane operation. Built in the median of the expressway is a two-lane 24-foot pavement with electrically controlled gates. This permits traffic to flow on the reversible pavement in the direction of the heavier movement, south in the morning and north in the afternoon.

The Kennedy was the second spoke to be completed in Chicago's transportation wheel of expressways. These 19 miles of broad, gleaming concrete provide for rapid, safe and economical transportation which will endure for generations.

15. Kennedy Expressway, June, 1970
At Addison Station, the bending Kennedy Expressway shares the right of way with rapid transit.

16. Monroe Street, May 19, 1959
The view at Monroe Street as work nears completion.

17. Kennedy Expressway, 1962
Opened nearly ten years before rapid transit was completed in January, 1970, the expressway is shown here with the as yet unoccupied median strip.

18. Hubbard's Cave, September, 1960
Before opening, the Kennedy Expressway is shown passing under Hubbard Street with the Chicago and Northwestern Railroad on the upper level.

19. Kennedy Expressway,
Downtown section west of the Loop, looking north as shown in the finishing stages.

All photographs are on file with the Chicago Historical Society

15

16

17

18

19

The Calumet Skyway Toll Bridge

The Calumet Skyway Toll Bridge connects Chicago to
Philadelphia, New York and New England through a network
of interstate turnpikes. This non-stop roadway provides the
motorist with a route to the eastern seaboard which is
completely free of grade crossings, traffic signals and
pedestrians.

Aside from providing a direct link with the East, the Skyway
also serves to relieve the south Chicago street system from
ever increasing traffic and congestion particularly in the heavy
industrial areas.

Originally the route was planned as a connection to the
Outer Drive along the lake shore, with the provision that the
Skyway be restricted to passenger cars only. Realizing
however that ever increasing volume of commercial truck
traffic must be accommodated, it was considered necessary to
provide a facility which would accommodate all types of
vehicular traffic. A second route considered was the existing
right-of-way of the Baltimore & Ohio Railroad; this was
rejected owing to the narrow width and the fact that there was
no satisfactory solution to the problem of providing multiple
terminals for delivery of heavy volumes of mixed traffic in this
heavily congested area.

The location selected provides a direct route with suitable
ingress and egress near a number of major thoroughfares,
with a minimum of disturbance to residential, commercial and
industrial buildings and connects directly with the Dan Ryan
South Expressway. This unique seven mile expressway bridge
soaring 120 feet over the Calumet River was opened to traffic
on April 16, 1958.

20. Calumet Skyway Aerial, 1973
*Snow covers the Calumet area where the
Skyway Bridge crosses the Calumet River.*

21. Calumet Skyway Underview, 1958
*Large freighters such as this one have no
difficulty clearing the Skyway Bridge as
they enter the heavily industrialized
Calumet area.*

22. Skyway Toll Gates, 1958
*Landscaping was taking root as the bridge
opened for traffic.*

*All photographs are on file with the
Chicago Historical Society*

20

21

22

The Crosstown

Chicago's growth as one of the great cities of the world stems from its unique and historical position as a transportation center. Chicago has always pioneered in development of a modern balanced transportation system: rail, air, waterways and expressways. The Crosstown Expressway is the final link in the Comprehensive Superhighway System.

A Crosstown Expressway on the west side of Chicago was described in Burnham's Plan as a "carriage road" to connect the various arms of the radial road system and relieve congestion in the central Loop area. The persistent need for this final link in the roadway system as originally set forth by Burnham at the turn of the century has been recommended by all major transportation planning commissions including the Comprehensive Expressway Plan of 1946, the Chicago Area Transportation Study (CATS) released in 1962, endorsed in 1963 as part of the Federal Interstate System to serve as a by-pass of the Central Business District and was incorporated into the Basic Policies for the Comprehensive Plan for Chicago published in 1964.

To determine whether it was necessary to construct this route within the near future, a general study of traffic congestion and other pertinent factors was carried out in the event it might be possible to substitute other types of improvements. This study convincingly demonstrated that if an expressway were not built within the next few years, traffic conditions on many adjacent streets would border on the intolerable. Not only would auto exhaust pollution reach critical levels, but the commercial and economic life of the city would be seriously impaired.

In the past, many highways have been located and designed solely on the basis of traffic requirements and economic consideration, with little or no regard for social aspects or future city planning. While roads are built to satisfy the need to move people and goods, they also have substantial social, psychological and economic impact on the communities which they run through or adjoin. Adequate consideration must be given to the objectives of the citizenry as a whole, and to future generations. An expressway development, such

23. High Accessibility Corridors
The structure of Chicago's high intensity-high density traffic pattern is illustrated on this schematic diagram. The Comprehensive Plan calls for construction of the concentric Crosstown Expressway to complete a logical traffic system.

All photographs are on file with the Chicago Historical Society

as the Crosstown, affords the opportunity to attract new industries, stimulate commercial activity, remove blight and upgrade neighborhoods.

With these new modern approaches to planning, the Crosstown was designed not only as an accommodation to traffic demand, but as a contribution to improved community life by minimizing disruption to neighborhoods and by provision for long-range development. Detailed design and specific route selection for this final and vital link in Chicago's history cannot proceed until federal approval of the recommended route has been received.

23

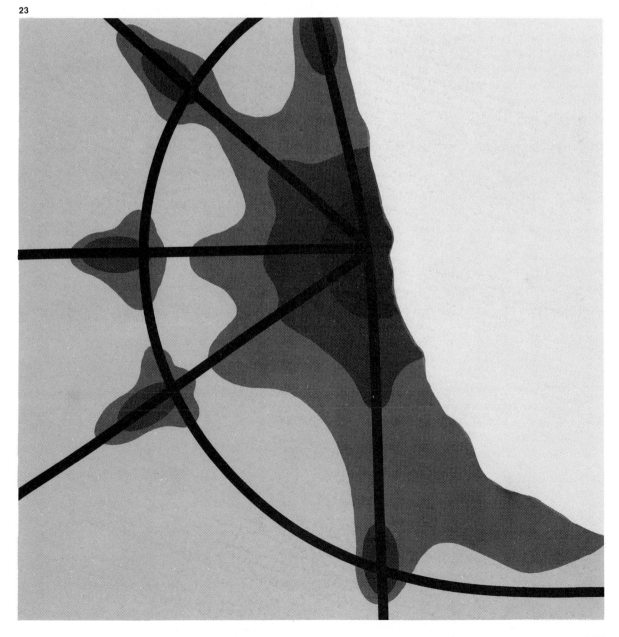

Parking Garages 11

Aerial View O'Hare Garage   January, 1973
So immense is this world's largest parking garage that it can only be seen in its entirety from the air. The four stacks of circular ramps in the center lead to the various levels. The new airport hotel, shown in crescent shape next to the control tower, separates the garage from the terminal buildings.

Municipal Parking

By the early 1950s, the lack of parking facilities in the central business area created a nuisance and hazard to traffic circulation. The City formed a parking authority with the assignment to acquire open lots on the fringes of the business district and to construct garages in the Loop area. This activity was financed by a $50 million revenue bond.

The largest garage was a five level ramp structure on Wacker Drive with a 1230 car capacity. Higher level garages were built using elevator access. A 12 level structure for short term parking of 495 cars was built on LaSalle across from City Hall. A 14 level structure, the world's largest elevator garage, with a 715 car capacity was built on Wacker Drive at State Street with access from both levels of Wacker Drive. In all 74 garages and lots were put into operation during the 1950's parking a total of 14,077 cars. By 1972 the preponderance of cars in the Loop reached a critical level; an ordinance was passed preventing the construction of further parking garages to discourage auto traffic in the downtown area.

1. Parking Facility No. 6, 1956
This garage, at 259 E. Superior Street, is now history. In 1972, this 1204 car, two-building facility was sold to Northwestern University and was demolished to make way for a hospital. The new medical complex will include a 2,000 car garage.

2. Private Parking Device, 1941
A number of innovative techniques were implemented by private interests to solve the parking problems. One was this elevator lot at Monroe near State. These were not economically viable and it was necessary for the City to undertake a parking program.

3. Parking Facility No. 5, 1955
At the northwest corner of Delaware Place and Rush Street is this 8 level structure holding 420 cars.

4, 5. Parking Facility No. 1, 1956
Called affectionately the "Bird Cage" because of the architectural design, this 14 story structure is the world's largest elevator garage. The sculpture by Milton Horn, shown adjacent, is entitled "Chicago Story," depicting the history of Chicago rising beside the Lake.

6. Parking Facility No. 8, 1954
This twelve level garage is for short term parking, located on LaSalle Street across from City Hall.

All photographs are on file with the Chicago Historical Society

1

The O'Hare Parking Garage

The world's largest parking garage is under construction for the world's busiest airport, O'Hare Field. When completed, the garage will accommodate over 12,500 autos in one central parking facility.

Groundbreaking on the facility was begun in spring, 1970, with the largest single construction contract ever awarded by the City of Chicago. Not only is this electronically operated garage the world's largest, but also one of the most technologically advanced. A brief review of its features gives some idea of the innovative design work that went into the $38 million project. The building curves approximately 1,432 feet across the south half of the existing main parking lot, leaving room for about 3,200 cars in the remaining north half of the lot.

Six levels of concrete decking total about 79 acres, with an additional five and one-half acres of basement space available for future expansion of terminal services. One possible utilization of this space would be as terminal area with ticketing and baggage check-in/check-out center. Enplaning and deplaning passengers would ride in a "people mover system" between the basement and departure gates through a network of underground tunnels.

Access to the garage is via the existing parking lot entrance/exit underpass where some of the toll booths are being removed to provide three entrance lanes for fast moving traffic. When the garage is completed, motorists will be able to drop off passengers on the upper level roadway as before and recirculate to the parking entrance underpass. Concrete curbs separating the short-term and rent-a-car areas can be removed and rebuilt anywhere to allow for increased allocation of space which will be leased to rent-a-car agencies. Eight stairways extending from the outer walls of the building will provide the emergency exits and alternate access to the facility.

Overhead electronically-controlled signs direct motorists to the proper lanes, and signs guide motorists to the appropriate one of two circular ramp systems. Garage traffic is controlled by automatic electronic detectors, counters and signs. To

7. Parking Ramps November, 1972
Ramps leading to the O'Hare International Airport parking structure were opened in December, shortly after this picture was taken, accommodating 5,000 of the new garage's 9250 parking spaces. The remaining 4250 parking spaces were completed in 1973. The six decks of the parking structure total 79 acres, making this the largest parking structure in the world. Electronic equipment will control snow melting equipment and assure adequate ventilation on the various levels. Constructing the world's largest two-way, post-tensioned beam and slab system required new construction techniques. Previously, to pour a 1200 cubic yard deck, required two cranes, and three placement crews, a total of 10 hours or 120 cubic feet per hour. With a newly developed crane having a 113-foot tower and a 150 foot boom, one placement crew can pour 225 cubic feet per hour keeping 11 cement trucks in continuous shuttle. The result is improved construction at lower cost.

All photographs are on file with the Chicago Historical Society

eliminate large backups of incoming cars at the underpass, automatic ticket dispensers are being installed at the entrance of each level. Queuing space is provided on the entrance lanes on each floor to eliminate backups on the ramps. Electronic detectors at parking entrances and exits keep an accurate count of cars.

A master control board in the manager's office houses all the electrical controls for the parking facility. These controls include a surveillance panel for all traffic control equipment, a carbon monoxide monitoring panel, standpipe alarm annunciator system, snow melting and ventilation pushbuttons, breaker alarm buttons and other devices. If both floors served by a single ramp become full, the overhead sign at the elevated roadway shows the ramp to be closed.

Each floor of the garage is divided into two sections. Six strategically located pedestrian centers are located on each floor of the garage. Each terminal building is to be served by two pedestrian centers and large illuminated signs throughout the garage point the way to the pedestrian center closest to each airline. Each pedestrian center will contain six elevators traveling at speeds of 300 feet per minute to transport over 2,700 people per hour.

Again, looking toward the future, it is estimated that the garage's eleven toll gates will reach capacity in the early 1970's. At that time, it is contemplated that a precashiering system will be employed similar to the one used in the Grant Park underground garages. The cashiers would be relocated to the basement and motorists would pay the parking fee before boarding elevators. They would hand over their receipt stubs at the toll gates, thereby considerably increasing the capacity of the gates.

Other features will include an emergency phone system with extensions at all pedestrian centers, ticket dispenser stations and toll booths. Persons requiring assistance need only pick up the receiver. A switchboard operator in the manager's office handles all calls. Temporary pay phones are located near pedestrian centers at the grade level and will be installed in the basement when that becomes a public area.

Much thought has gone into the parking garage's signs. Illuminated exit signs are used throughout the facility. Pedestrian center and traffic control signs are plastic face illuminated exit signs. Traffic control signs have neon messages superimposed over plastic face messages, and switch messages automatically in conjunction with differential counters. Pedestrians are directed towards pedestrian centers by following directions to their airlines. "You Are Here" signs are located at all pedestrian center entrances. All graphics in the facility are coordinated with existing O'Hare Terminal signs.

Apart from being the largest elevated parking facility ever built, the structure presents an interesting structural design

8. Constructing the Garage, 1972
Workmen shown here make use of the world's largest crane, a 113-foot tower with a 150-foot boom. This conveyor system can pour 225 cubic yards of concrete per hour keeping eleven trucks busy in a continuous shuttle. With equipment such as this, immense structures can be constructed in shorter time periods at premium quality with reduced costs.

concept. The parking decks comprising a two-way beam and slab system were post-tensioned. The structural lightweight concrete utilizing expansive cement was used for decks and columns above the grade level. These design features resulted in a sizable reduction in dead load and therefore increased economy in construction and additional usable revenue space.

Public Transportation   12

The Elevated on Wabash 1972
*Soon to be a part of history books and
memories, the Loop Elevated will be
replaced within the decade of the 70s by a
unique central area transit system. This
new system will be an integration of two
new subways: a shallow subway, called
the Distributor which will coordinate with
a new deep subway and with older
existing subways to give Chicago a
coordination of transportation modes
unique in the nation.*

177

Early Chicago Transit

The horse drawn Omnibus moved only about 6 miles per hour, or about twice as fast as a man could walk. The introduction of this small coach in 1850 was therefore sufficient to double the size of the community. Later rails were laid on the most heavily traveled routes and horse-drawn street railways were introduced. By 1856, 18 lines were making more than 400 trips daily.

The cable car was introduced from San Francisco in the 1870s. Although the cable car was faster and cleaner than the horse drawn vehicles, objections and protests were bitterly waged against its installation. People worried that the cars were too fast and would injure and frighten people and horses alike. Others felt the first fears of automation. Some worried that the high cost, of about $100,000 per mile, would lead to uncontrolled inflation. Nevertheless, the first cable car installed on State Street in 1882 was an instant success. By 1895 Chicago had 86 miles of cable cars in service. Introduction of the cable car along a line replacing a former horse-drawn system meant an instant increase in property evaluations. However, the electric trolley, introduced in 1892, rapidly gained favor. By 1893 more than 500 miles of mass transit tracks carried 200 million riders a year and the days of the cable car were numbered.

The Columbian Exposition stimulated new transit development. The first elevated was put in use in 1890 and service reached the exposition grounds by 1893 to carry Fair patrons. The "Loop" system serving the downtown business district was operational by 1897; the last cable car was withdrawn from service in 1906.

Bitter competition for operating franchises had characterized the early days of rapid transit development. Gradually, the lines were consolidated and by 1913 the entire system, covering nearly 1,000 miles of track, was under one line, the Chicago Surface Lines. At a time when most everyone lived within two blocks of some form of mass transit, and when ridership increased yearly with increasing population, the encroachment of the automobile had already begun.

1. Omnibus, 1853
Although not a part of organized public transportation, and operating without an ordinance, the Omnibus was a familiar sight in Chicago and ran from downtown to what is now Lincoln Park beginning in 1850. Scheduled routes came later with the Omnibus Line operating in competition with organized public transit. The Omnibus was replaced in the mid-1860s by the horse drawn rail car enfranchised in 1856.

2. Bobtail, 1859
Chicago's first form of organized local public transportation was the horse drawn car operating on State Street, purchased second-hand from New York City. It was named the Bobtail for the small platform in the rear which passengers used while boarding or leaving the car.

3. Summer Car, mid-1860s
This summer car was one of the first cars to appear on Chicago streets where it served for nearly 50 years. At the time of this photograph, the car was used on the Fullerton and Halsted Line and carries an advertisement for a picnic. The last horse drawn car was withdrawn from service in 1906. Aside from sanitation problems involved with several thousand horses on the streets, horses averaged only about four miles per hour as compared with cable car's possible 14 miles per hour. The term "Loop" used for the central business district is believed to have originated with the horse cars and cable cars which formed a loop with their tracks to eliminate use of the turn tables during the 1880s.

4. Steam-Dummy Rail Service, 1864
Named for the dummy housing which covered the steam locomotive used to avoid frightening horses, this service operated during the 1860s and 1870s.

5. Single Truck Car, 1900s
The open single truck streetcars were obtained in the 1890s and lasted until 1914. This one was on the Belmont route.

6. Closed Car, 1896
Typical closed car, built as a trailer in 1800s, and electrified in 1896.

1

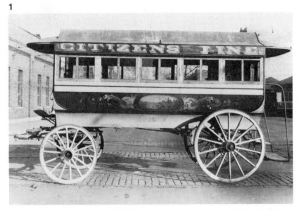

2

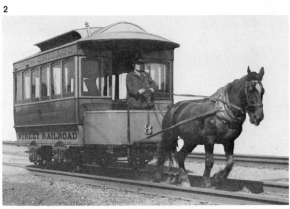

3

4

5

6

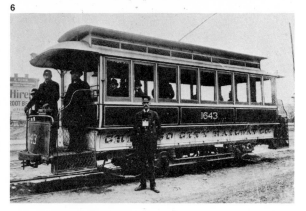

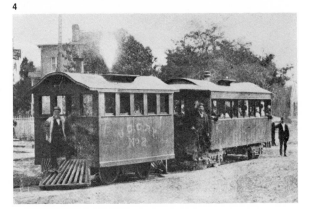

Decline

The automobile age is generally considered to have begun in 1903, the year of the organization of the Ford Motor Company. By 1916, there were more than 3.6 million registered vehicles. It is worth noting that until 1926 the revenue passengers on the nation's public transportation facilities increased in direct proportion to the population. By 1926, the ratio of people to registered vehicles was 11 to 1, and since that year as the ratio declined, the number of public transportation riders declined. The one exception was the wartime imposed gasoline rationing during which the nation's transit riders increased.

Mass transportation companies throughout the nation found they could not make ends meet; any attempt to raise the fare to cover costs of operation generally resulted in a reduction of riders and a loss of revenue. Chicago was no exception.

Today, every metropolitan area faces strangulation by private vehicles transporting one or two bodies when a train or bus can hold many more in the same space. A public transit system not only relieves the congestion of auto traffic, but finally results in a radical reduction of air pollutants in the urban atmosphere.

For more than a half century, Chicago had been struggling to solve its local transit problems. The situation reached a critical stage in the late 20s when the Chicago Surface Lines and the Chicago Rapid Transit Company became involved in receivership and bankruptcy proceedings. In 1945, after failure of six separate and prolonged attempts to reorganize the two companies with the aid of private capital, State and City officials suggested the establishment of a public authority to acquire, own and operate the city's local transit facilities as the only practical solution of the city's traffic problems.

7. Cable Car Cutaway View
This early drawing explained to the public how the cable car operated. Service began in 1882, under heavy public protest by those who thought the fast moving cars would frighten the horses.

8. Chicago Day on a Cable Car, October 8, 1893
The greatest traffic day in Chicago transit history occurred on Chicago Day at the World's Columbian Exposition. The Illinois Central Railroad alone carried more than a half-million passengers, which has not been equaled since. All transit lines were swamped. Since cable cars had no roof trolley wires, passengers rode atop the car. This scene is on the 3800 Block on Cottage Grove.

9. Cottage Grove Cable Car, 1890s
Running in trains of from one to five cars, this line went from 55th Street at Lake Park to the Loop and served the Columbian Exposition in Jackson Park. With open cars for summer use and closed cars for winter, the cable cars were an instant success and nearly five hundred were in operation at peak usage during the late 1890s. The electric streetcar quickly took over operation and the last cable car was removed in 1906.

10. Lake Street Elevated, 1893
The steam powered elevated was limited to four cars. Conversion to electric power came in 1896.

11. Funeral Car, 1905
Because cemeteries were located at some distance from the city, a distance too far for most horse drawn wagons or early automobiles, special street cars were used for funerals between 1910 and 1919. Elevated funeral cars were also in use between 1905 and 1932.

12. The Electrified Elevated, 1900
Always one of the great sightseeing tours in the world, the electric elevated is shown looking west on Van Buren. Electrification of all horse and cable car routes went at a rapid pace after the turn of the century.

All photographs are on file with the Chicago Historical Society

7

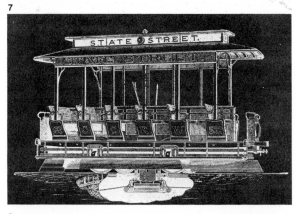

8

11

9

10

12

The Chicago Transit Authority

The principal local mass transportation carrier within the city of Chicago is the Chicago Transit Authority, operating the second largest public transit system in North America. The CTA serves all section of Chicago and 34 suburbs within Cook County. Ninety-nine percent of the City's population is within 3/8 mile of CTA service.

The Chicago Transit Authority is a self-regulating municipal corporation, separate and apart from all other governmental agencies. It was created in 1945 by an Act of the Illinois General Assembly and an ordinance of the Chicago City Council, and was confirmed by local referendum. The ordinance grants exclusive right to CTA for operation of a comprehensive unified local transportation system in Chicago.

CTA policies are made by the Chicago Transit Board, consisting of seven members, four of whom are appointed by the Mayor of Chicago, and three by the Governor of Illinois.

The Authority, as a corporate entity, has the power to acquire, construct, own, operate and maintain for public service, a transportation system in the metropolitan area of Cook County. Subsequent to the original Act, amendments were made to permit acquisition of rail transit facilities extending outward beyond that limit if they connect with its rapid transit system and to contract to operate common carriers or the systems of local Mass Transit Districts outside that limit.

CTA began operations in 1947 by purchasing the properties of the Chicago Surface lines and the Chicago Rapid Transit Company. In 1952, it purchased the Chicago Motor Coach Company. A year later CTA purchased from the Chicago, Milwaukee, St. Paul and Pacific Railroad the elevated line from Montrose Avenue, Chicago, to Linden Avenue, Wilmette, on which the rapid transit had operated under a lease. Purchase of all of these properties was not financed by public money, but by the sale of revenue bonds to private investors. Approximately $57 million of such long-term debt was outstanding at the close of 1970.

Service is provided on 135 bus routes over 2000 miles of city and suburban streets and on six rapid transit routes over

13. Streetcar in Low Density Area, 1890
Public transportation, like any public service, must serve the public's interest regardless of profit-potential. In this scene in Oak Park, houses were few and far between on West Madison. The speed of the streetcar made long distance commuting feasible in terms of the pace of the time.

14. Green Hornet, 1947
Known for their color, increased speed and rapid acceleration, 600 of these were purchased in 1946. By the time streetcar service was terminated in 1958, a total of 570 of these cars had been salvaged for use as rapid transit cars.

15. Flooding September 21, 1947
Trolley cars remain in service during one of the city's worst storms. The Madison Street car is shown here passing through an underpass on the West Side.

16. Red Pullman Car
One of the city's biggest passenger carriers, this car seated 40 and had standing room for 116 more. Curved sides were designed to pass horse-drawn vehicles and wagons. These cars ran until 1954. The first streetcars appeared in 1890 and quickly dominated the scene for more than a half century, with some lines in use for 99 years. Streetcars reached a peak during the 1930s when 3,742 clanged their way over 60 different routes.

17. Double-Deck Bus, 1923
Sunday trips along Lake Shore Drive were just one of the special rides available on this handsome bus which frequented the boulevards. The bus carried 39 passengers on the roof and 28 inside. The hard rubber tires shown here were replaced in 1928; this model retired from service in 1937.

All photographs are on file with the Chicago Historical Society

approximately 90 miles of subway and surface rights-of-way. 75% of these routes operate around the clock every day. Approximately 2700 motor and trolley buses and 1200 rapid transit cars are operated.

On a typical weekday, the Authority serves about 1.2 million revenue passengers, of whom about 400,000 originate on the six rapid transit lines, while the balance originate on buses. About 750,000 passengers per weekday purchase transfers which entitle them to extend their trips over interconnecting CTA bus or rapid transit routes. Counting each rider, including those with transers and those who travel under special arrangement without fare, the City transports over 600 million riders per year.

The cornerstone of the CTA is the rapid transit system. Chicago pioneered use of expressway median strips for the grade-separated rail transit, operating successfully on the Kennedy, Dan Ryan and Eisenhower expressways. One-fourth of the Kennedy rapid transit is in subway. This rail service is in addition to the conventional subway system and the famous elevated.

Another unique feature of the expressway rapid transit is the interchange terminal design which places the facility wholly within the air rights of the rail system. These terminals are built over the outside slopes of the roadway and provide sufficient, inter-modal transfer facilities.

A variety of patron conveniences are incorporated into the terminal design: short cut passageways with escalators, common loading bays and canopied interchange areas with connecting shuttle bus services.

To make the rapid transit stations intermodal interchange points, part of the historic grid of parallel bus routes was rearranged to form neighborhood oriented radial networks, converging on the rapid transit terminals. An immediate result of this newly formed "feeder" network was an increase in ridership of 26,000 per day, with another 140,000 riders changing routes and shortening length of ride time.

Park-N-Ride facilities have also been added to the terminals of rapid transit lines. The lack of adequate parking at many of the terminals is considered as one of the most seriously limiting constraints to the present system.

The speed, convenience and dependability of the rapid transit service attract over 150 million riders per year. Over the years, ridership has not decreased, as with other services, but has generally held steadily, increasing when improvements become operational.

In principle, the bus is a more flexible vehicle than the rapid transit since the bus is not bound to a fixed rail. Although the bus is admittedly flexible in terms of route selection, it must compete for space on the street with the automobile. Traffic delays reduce speed, convenience and dependability, factors all important in mass transit. At average load factors, a bus

18. Fare History, 1947–1970
As ridership declines, individual fares increase causing further decline and fare increases. Inflationary pressures on salaries are another cause of financial concern. Income balanced expenses for the last time in 1962 when salaries accounted for only 62 percent of income; by 1972, salaries consumed 82 percent of income and spiraling deficits spelled the end of a purely fare box operation.

19. The Loop Elevated June, 1972
The present "L" structure is to be replaced by a new $760 million subway system currently under design through an initial $5.8 million federal grant. The new Central Area Rapid Transit System, will also link suburban rail and rapid transit stations providing an integrated modern transportation system for downtown Chicago.

20. Escalators, Northwest Passage, 1972
Taking the Northwest Passage escalator down to a connecting CTA bus helps minimize transfer time for commuting suburbanities on the Chicago and Northwestern Railway. This link affords suburban railroad passengers broad distribution throughout the Central Business District.

21. The Skokie Swift, 1972
The Skokie Swift, a pilot project under a federally funded demonstration grant, developed and tested a high-speed two-station commuter shuttle along a previously abandoned five mile portion of railway. As part of the CTA, the line serves 8,000 suburban passengers per week day and is self sustaining. Park-and-Ride facilities as well as connecting suburban and Greyhound buses are provided at the terminal.

CTA fare increases

With transfer ___

											55c
50c
										45c	
40c
								40c		
							35c			
30c
					30c				
20c
			25c					
10c | 11c | 13c | 15c | 17c | 20c | | | | | |
10c

1947 '48 '48 '49 '51 '52 '57 '61 '67 '68 '70

18

20

19

21

185

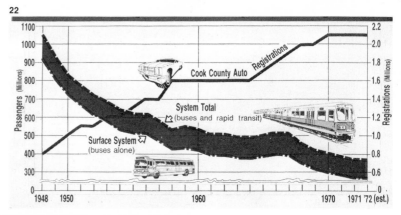

22

23

24

22. Ridership History 1948–1971
As car registrations climb, passengers in public transit decline. In 1948, the Chicago Transit Authority had over one billion passengers. If all transfers are counted, including passengers from suburban railroads, the system still provides nearly two million rides per day.

23. Kennedy Rapid Transit, 1973
New and old transit car pass beside the congested Kennedy Expressway. The City received 150 new cars in 1970 as part of the Urban Mass Transportation Act of 1964.

24. Dan Ryan 95th Station, 1972
The 95th Street terminal on the Dan Ryan Expressway, contained in the right-of-way of the grade-separated rail service in the expressway median strip, connects with 13 suburban bus routes. Patron conveniences include attractive and efficient high-illumination lighting, escalators, infra-red heaters, a translucent canopy, Park-and-Ride facilities and common loading bays.
Rapid transit stations on the Kennedy and Dan Ryan lines won two design awards—A Biennial Design Award from the Department of Housing and Urban Development and an Honorable Mention for creative multiple use of Expressway Right-of-Way in the Department of Transportation's competition "The Highway and its Environment."

25. Up the Middle, 1972
Rapid transit in the median strip of the Eisenhower Expressway, a Chicago innovation.

26. Clark Street Traffic, 1972
Mid-morning traffic on Clark near Randolph. The Sherman House, to the right, closed for demolition shortly after this picture was taken.

27. Snow Storm Commuters, December 1972
Morning commuter rush hour after a surprise snow storm at the Belmont Station on the elevated system.

All photographs are on file with the Chicago Historical Society

25

26

27

takes only 6 square feet of space per passenger moved, compared to 75 square feet per passenger for an automobile. If it were not for the automobile in its path, a bus could move its passengers in speed, comfort and economy over a smaller roadway network at a much lower total system cost.

Preferential treatment of busses is essential if the bus service is to increase in speed and dependability. In Chicago, two types of exclusive lane use are in operation: a "reverse only" lane used at the Union and Northwestern stations and a "bus only" lane located in the center land of one-way Washington Street. Studies have shown that the time savings is substantial. For example, the bus-only lane across the Loop requires less than half the time required by a bus in conventional traffic.

A great variety of efficiency and economy measures have been identified and made operational. The use of intermodal common loading bays, deletion of route duplication and numerous other scheduling arrangements are being used as aids in convenience and service to the patron.

28. Dan Ryan Rapid Transit, 1972
Serving Chicago's southside commuters, the Dan Ryan Rapid Transit line extends 9.5 miles from the 95th Street Station to the downtown terminal, taking approximately 20 minutes for the entire route. The Dan Ryan line was the second expressway to utilize grade-separated median strips for rapid transit, following the successful introduction of this approach on the Eisenhower Expressway.

29. Jefferson Park Terminal, 1972
An aerial view of the Jefferson Park Terminal on the Kennedy Expressway is one example of the unique and successful concept of placing interchange terminals above the rail right-of-way, within the air rights of the median strip. Connecting to suburban buses and rail service, the Kennedy serves 165,000 passengers per week day.

30. Common Loading Bay, 1972
The sheltered common loading bay at Jefferson Street Station on the Kennedy Expressway typifies the emphasis on efficient inter-modal transfer facilities.

31. Englewood Terminal, 1972
The Englewood Terminal, at 63rd and Ashland replaces the former terminal built in 1907. 2,500 patrons use the terminal daily; a 250-car capacity Park-and-Ride facility is available. The Englewood control tower is specifically designed for rush hour conditions. An automatic control system is included for adding or taking out cars on the rapid transit line.

32. Exclusive Bus Lane, 1972
One of the exclusive bus lanes in Chicago's central business district is on downtown, one-way, heavily utilized Washington Street. Such lanes move passengers at approximately twice the speed of conventional traffic and promote an orderly and well regulated flow of auto traffic in adjacent lanes.

All photographs are on file with the Chicago Historical Society

29

30

31

32

189

The Subways

Chicago's two subways, completed in 1943 and 1951 respectively, were built at a cost of $75 million of which nearly $26 million was contributed by the federal government. The City's share was provided by a fund built up over the years by payments from passenger revenues from privately owned transit companies for franchises to operate local services. Both the State Street and the West Side Subways are owned by the City of Chicago and operated by the Chicago Transit Authority as major units of its rapid transit system.

Together the two subways provide 17.2 miles of underground rapid transit trackage and facilities. Vast quantities of materials were used in building them—150,000 tons of steel. 1,250,000 barrels of cement, 1,250,000 cubic yards of sand and stone, 300 miles of conduit, and large amounts of other materials. More than 2,500,000 cubic yards of clay were excavated in tunneling the tubes and building the mezzanine stations.

Work on the city's first subway began December 17, 1938. A deep shaft was excavated for access to the line of the subway where mining operations began.

Mining through the soft, watery clay underlying the city was a difficult engineering task but it was accomplished without a single cave-in or loss of heading. Compressed air 10 to 15 pounds above atmospheric pressure was used to help support the clay walls of the tubes. A lock erected in each tunnel drift prevented the compressed air from escaping. Men and materials went through the lock to and from the tubes while mining was in progress. Because of the Loop's fluid soil, the tubes in this area were mined by heavy, cylindrical steel devices called shields, each weighing about 225 tons. In shield mining, the clay walls of the tube were supported both by the shield and heavy rings of steel lining as well as by compressed air. Consequently the possibility of cave-ins was reduced to a minimum.

In the outlying area, where the clay subsoil is relatively firm, the tubes were mined by the "Bench" method. Using heavy curved knives that pulled through the clay by air power, the miners shaped the tubes. Mining proceeded on three levels (benches) generally. Each crew, had from twenty to thirty men

33. **Tunnel Construction 1940**
View of tunnel shield and heading during regular mining operations.

34. **Jackson Station, 1943**
State Street Subway showing illumination "light enough to read by".

All photographs are on file with the Chicago Historical Society

190

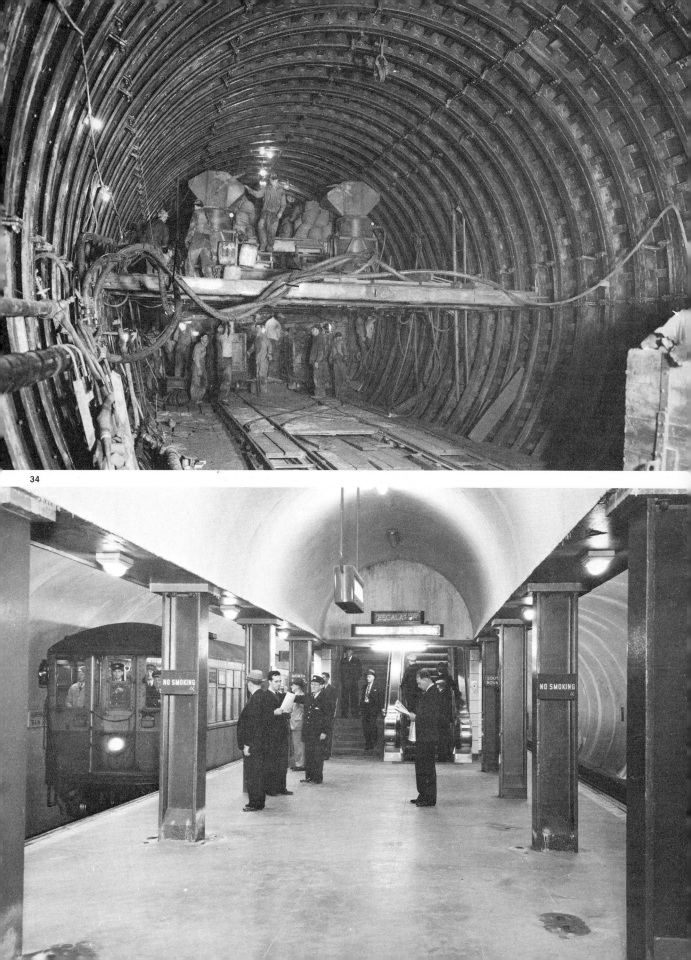

34

in the average day working in three eight-hour shifts. The progess averaged about twenty-five feet of tube each 24 hours.

Mining methods in the construction of both horseshoe and circular tubes provided for maximum protection against collapse. Supporting clay walls with liner plates and steel ribs was one important precautionary measure. This was followed by the erection of a lattice-work of reinforcing steel around which the concrete for the walls was poured. In the Loop much heavier lining was used. Concrete mixed on the street surface was forced through large pipes either by pneumatic pressure or by special concrete pumps, sometimes as far as a thousand feet to final placement in steel forms. All walls, floors and roofs were of thick concrete, heavily reinforced with steel bars and backed up by continuous steel liner plates and ribs.

Construction of the tubes under the river posed difficult but interesting engineering problems. It was necessary to avoid a steep grade in the approach to the Lake Street Station. The problem was solved by building a section of twin tubes in dry dock and towing it to the site of the crossing where it was lowered into a deep trench previously dug in the bed of the river. Connections with the tubes on either side of the river were then constructed in cofferdams.

Mezzanine stations and crossovers in the tubes were constructed by the open cut method. This consisted of an excavation in the street in which the structure was built. As soon as the depth of the excavation permitted, it was covered with heavy decking to carry the normal traffic of the street above with minimum interference during the course of construction. Underneath the decking, work proceeded. Subsurface facilities and street car tracks were relocated temporarily. Incline connections with the "L" were excavated on acquired property.

On the north, the subway joins the "L" just south of the Armitage Avenue Station. Entering and leaving the subway, as well as in the tubes, the trains are protected at all times by the most modern type of signal equipment. Trains must be operated to conform with the speeds for which the signal system is set. Failure to obey a red signal automatically causes the brakes to be applied on every car.

The Milwaukee-Dearborn-Congress Subway extends a distance of 3.99 miles from a connection with the Logan Square elevated structure near Damen and Milwaukee Avenues, southeastward under Milwaukee to Lake Street, east under Lake to Dearborn, south to Congress and west under Congress to a downtown terminal at LaSalle Street. A two-track subway, it emerges in the vicinity of Halsted Street and continues westward to a point near South Lotus Avenue (5432 West), as a rapid transit line in the median strip of the Eisenhower superhighway.

35. Subway, 1943
Jackson Station in the State Street Subway as train approaches.

36. Subway Escalator, 1943
New escalators are well used by subway patrons.

All photographs are on file with the Chicago Historical Society

35

36

The new tube, built at a cost of approximately $40 million, is Route No. 2 of Chicago's Initial System of Subways. This figure represented the total cost of the completed subway, ready for revenue operation. Included were the basic construction of tubes, stations and structures, architectural finish, lighting, acquisition of right-of-way, engineering, as well as such operating equipment as track, signals, power, communciation and emergency alarm systems. The operating equipment cost approximately $5 million.

Construction of Route No. 2 was started on March 15, 1939, and continued simultaneously with the State Street project until 1942 when work was halted because of material shortages arising out of World War II. Route No. 2 was 80 per cent completed at that time. With the war over, construction activities were resumed on March 25, 1946. The subway was completed and opened for service February 25, 1951.

In 1970, voters paved the way for a new subway system by passing a referendum creating a special tax district which would help finance a subway study to replace the antiquated "L" structures in the Loop. Called the Central Area Transit Project, the proposed system will consist of two major subway facilities: (1) an east-west high level shuttle or distributor subway from the University of Illinois Campus on the near west side via Monroe Street to two branches along the lakefront and (2) a conventional subway in a loop pattern under existing subways in the Loop area. Improved subway connections in the north and west and a connection to the Dan Ryan rapid transit route are included. New rapid transit cars and the elimination of the Loop elevated structures will contribute to the suppression of noise pollution. In 1972, a federal grant for $5.8 million was provided to finance the systems analysis and management phase, with completion of the facility scheduled by the end of this decade.

37. Logan Square Subway Station, 1972
Vaulted celings at the Logan Square Station on the Kennedy Rapid Transit line replace the column cluttered subway platforms of another era. The high illumination and absence of obstructions provide a safe and attractive station connecting directly with feeder buses.

38. Kennedy Subway, 1972
Escalators, modern lighting, and stainless steel rapid transit cars on welded rails cushioned on stressed-concrete ties and stone ballasts all add to the safety and efficiency of the Logan Square Kennedy Rapid Transit line. All stations built after 1970 have escalators.

39. Central Area Subway Project, 1973
The Distributor System, a new shallow subway, will coordinate with a new deep subway and with older existing subways to greatly increase the viability of Chicago's central business district. This project will bring to Chicago a coordination of transportation modes unique in the nation.

All photographs are on file with the Chicago Historical Society

37

38

39

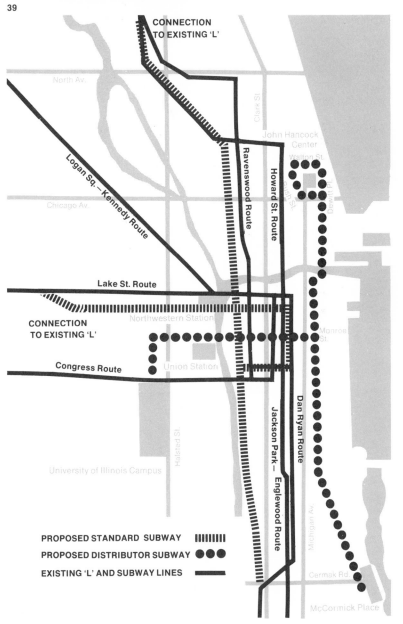

CONNECTION TO EXISTING 'L'

Logan Sq. – Kennedy Route

Ravenswood Route

Howard St. Route

John Hancock Center

Walton St.

DeWitt Pl.

North Av.

Clark St.

Chicago Av.

Lake St. Route

Northwestern Station

CONNECTION TO EXISTING 'L'

Monroe St.

Congress Route

Union Station

Halsted St.

University of Illinois Campus

Jackson Park – Englewood Route

Dan Ryan Route

Michigan Av.

Cermak Rd.

McCormick Place

PROPOSED STANDARD SUBWAY ||||||||

PROPOSED DISTRIBUTOR SUBWAY   ●●●

EXISTING 'L' AND SUBWAY LINES   ━━━

The Bicycle as Urban Transportation

Chicago was the first metropolitan center to test the principle of bikeways in a major way. This pioneer network covers 100 miles of lakefront paths through four parks, plus an extensive inland route covering city streets and some 25 inland parks, as 10,000 cyclists per day crowd the paths on pleasant weekends.

Whether cycling in neighborhoods or commuting into the Loop, Chicagoans in greater numbers have indicated their desire to bicycle for enjoyment, exercise and economy, as well as to reduce traffic congestion and help curb noise and air pollution caused by auto emissions.

These bike routes are designated by 24 × 18-inch rectangular trail marker signs with a white legend consisting of a bicycle symbol, the words "BIKE ROUTE", and a border in white on a green background, fully reflectorized. They are supplemented with directional arrows placed below the route guide signs where needed. Typically, one trail blazer is installed per block in each direction.

Besides directing the bicyclist along the proper route, the signs inform the cyclist that the bike route marked is safer than nearby alternate routes he might choose for himself. They also warn other traffic to proceed cautiously since bicyclists may be encountered.

Generally, the bike routes chosen follow the city's quartermile streets with lower traffic volumes, which are wide enough to accommodate bicyles and motor vehicles, and which are already equipped with traffic control devices at most major street intersections. Street speed limits, over and underpasses across major roadways and hidden dangers such as storm drains with wide gratings are other factors that are being considered in choosing the best safety route locations.

The Chicago Bicycle Route System will eventually connect most neighborhoods, inland parks, forest preserves, community and outlying recreation facilities, schools, libraries, churches, local shopping areas and transportation terminals as feasible so that people may cycle to places they have formerly reached by car. Adequate and secure bike parking is provided at most city parking facilities which offer

40. Lake Shore Drive, 1972
Chicago's entire lake shore makes a continuous bike path.

41. Water Filtration Plant, 1972
One of the major attractions along Chicago's scenic lakefront bicycle paths is the Central Water Filtration Plant's ten-acre Olive Park.

42. Bike Lane Signs, 1972
Bike lanes are clearly designated as distinct from either traffic or pedestrian walks as indicated by this green and white sign. In the picture shown, the street is wide enough to accommodate a bike lane. In other locations, where wide sidewalks are available, portions of the sidewalk are designated for the bike lane.

43. Maps, 1972
Over 100 miles of bike paths and safety routes are available throughout Chicago.

All photographs are on file with the Chicago Historical Society

supervised racks. Outdoor racks are also provided where appropriate. In addition, other modes of bike storage are being studied and implemented in conjunction with active groups and the Bike Institute of America. Combined participation and cooperation are insuring the success of this new mode of urban transportation.

43

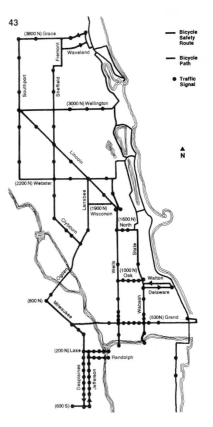

— Bicycle Safety Route

— Bicycle Path

● Traffic Signal

40

41

42

43

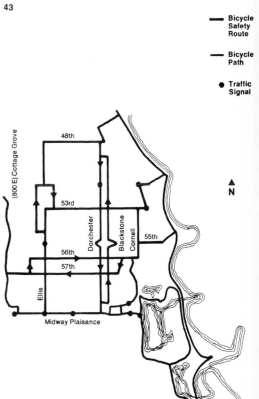

— Bicycle Safety Route

— Bicycle Path

● Traffic Signal

Airports

**Chicago-O'Hare International
Airport 1973**
*Approaching O'Hare Airport by air
highlights several of Public Work's most
extensive projects: the terminal complex,
itself capable of serving 90,000 people
each day, the control tower with
transparent radome, the unique airport
hotel built in a crescent adjacent to the
control tower and the world's largest
parking garage easily identifiable by the
set of four circular stacks of vehicle
ramps. As a transportation center, air
transport is of special interest to Chicago
and from earliest days, Chicago has been
an aggressive leader in air development*

Chicago Midway Airport

The early 1900's saw aviation enthusiasts gathering in Chicago. An International Aviation Meeting was sponsored in 1911 by prominent Chicagoans who offered $80,000 in prize money to attract the world's greatest aviators. The meeting, held at Grant Park, was witnessed by several million residents and considered the most impressive display of aviation ever presented.

Small private air fields dotted the city as flying became an acceptable mode of transportation. Charles Lindbergh was gaining experience as a pilot on the Chicago-St. Louis flight. By 1920 it was clear that Chicago needed a public airport.

In the early part of 1926, a resident of Chicago, Col. P. G. Kemp, arranged a lease on Board of Education property located in the southwestern corner of the city and constructed a hangar. He operated four airplanes, which were used for sightseeing, student flight instruction and charter. About the middle of 1926, the City of Chicago leased 120 acres of this property from the Board of Education. At the time the City of Chicago leased this property, there was one airplane hangar on the property, owned by Col. Kemp. In 1927, the City Council appropriated $10,000 for the construction and betterment of the airport, and for the salaries of operating personnel.

On December 1, 1927, the first contract airmail plane landed here. The contractor was Boeing Air Transport. The plane arrived from Omaha, Nebraska, piloted by Ira O. Bifflle, the man who taught Charles A. Lindbergh to fly. The field was dedicated on December 12, 1927.

1928 was the first full year of operation for Chicago Municipal Airport. In this one year, it became the busiest airport in the United States, boasting 12 airplane hangars, 4 well-marked and well-lighted cinder runways and up-to-date field lighting for night landings.

A bond issue of $450,000, voted in November 1930 was used for further construction and additional taxiways, runways, sewers and concrete ramps in front of the hangars. This permitted extension of the east-west runway from about 2,400 lineal feet to approximately 4,900 lineal feet. The extension of

1. Air Show, 1911
Air travel came to Chicago the same year the new City Hall was finished when fliers competed for $80,000 in prize money. Octave Chanute, the engineer who designed the Chicago Union Stockyards, was one of the organizers of this event, and was himself one of Chicago's aviation enthusiasts and designer of early heavier-than-air craft.

2. Municipal Airport, 1929
The humble beginnings of Midway Airport are evident from this early photograph, taken in the first year of operation. With coming of the Century of Progress in the early 1930's this airport quickly became the busiest airport in the world.

3. Midway Airport, January, 1973
With the new jets coming into use in the early 1960's, Midway flights decreased owing to the restricted runway length. However, with the development of lighter, smaller jets and construction of extended runways, Midway is once more growing.

All photographs are on file with the Chicago Historical Society

2

3

this runway was essential because the airlines were then using larger airplanes for the transport of passengers, and larger tri-motor Boeing and Ford airplanes, each with a capacity for handling large amounts of mail and express.

During 1932 traffic and operations continued to rise and at the end of the year it was found that Chicago Municipal Airport was not only the busiest airport in the United States, it was the busiest one in the world.

Newer and larger airplanes continued to be built through 1935 and Transcontinental & Western Air (TWA) inaugurated the first non-stop flight between Chicago and New York on January 9,1935, with a DC3, which made the trip in 4 hours and 5 minutes. On February 21, 1935, American Airlines commenced a transcontinental flight from Los Angeles to New York, via Chicago, with some other intermediate stops, and set a record flying time of 11 hours and 42 minutes. By 1936, seven airlines operated 114 daily flights.

Improvements were made over the years. In 1940, rail trackage that bisected the field was relocated. In 1945, when the new terminal was built, Chicago was certified for overseas flights to Europe. The name, Chicago Municipal Airport was changed to Midway in 1949, to commemorate the U.S. victory at Midway Island during World War II.

Midway continued to hold the title of world's busiest airport through 1950. Because of increasing congestion, air traffic began shifting to the newly constructed O'Hare as early as 1955 and by the end of 1962, scheduled operations were completely out of Midway. With the new jets coming in use the restriction of runway length was a vital factor.

However, by 1964, smaller and lighter jet aircraft were developed which could be accommodated by Midway's shorter runways. In 1964, United returned with the 727 tri-jet and 10 scheduled flights daily. Today, a total of approximately 120 scheduled flights are routinely handled.

Six operational runways approximately 6,500 feet long take non-stop flights from 800 to 1,000 miles. These currently handle DC-9, 737 twin jets, 727 tri-jets and the BAC-111, together with turbo jets such as the F-27 and Convair 440.

The resurgence of Midway is due in part to the easy access to the Chicago Loop area when driving time to the Loop was cut to about 20 minutes with the opening of the Stevenson Expressway. Connecting as it does to smaller, close-in municipal airports of other cities, the traveler finds excellent connections to business areas of major and medium sized cities throughout the Midwest and eastern seaboard.

4. Terminal Building, 1967
Portions of the old terminal building were removed to make way for a modern terminal with three concourses. Other improvements include new drainage from the apron area to handle storm run-off, as well as numerous runway improvements and general renovation throughout the field. Scheduled flights were discontinued on July 31, 1967 and were reopened in October, 1967.

5. Welcome Back Sign
Sign announcing the re-opening of Midway Airport following reconstruction.

6. Control Tower 1962
The FAA control tower maintains visual and electronic control of all aircraft movement at Midway Airport.

All photographs are on file with the Chicago Historical Society

4

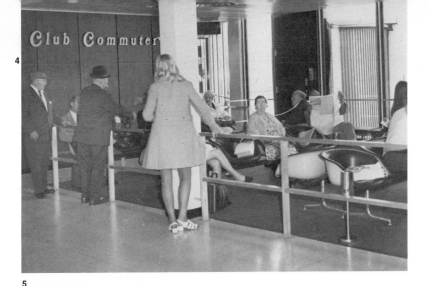

5

6

Chicago-O'Hare International Airport

With a greater runway capacity than any other airport in the country, it was realized by 1945 that with steadily increasing traffic the City must look ahead and acquire another airport to accommodate the greatly increased air traffic. A site selection committee of business and civic leaders, airline executives and engineers was appointed to make a survey of the Chicago area and given instructions to choose a site for a new airport.

In 1945 the Douglas Airport (Orchard Place), located just west of Mannheim Road and south of Higgins Road, was selected as that site. This property was built by the military and turned over to Douglas Aircraft Corporation for its assembly plant, taxiways and runways on June 30, 1942. The wartime work was completed August 31, 1943, consisting of four concrete runways, necessary taxiways, a large aircraft assembly building and an office and engineering building. The runways were 150 feet wide and varied in length from 5,500 to 5,700 feet. Between August 1943 and October, 1945, a total of 655 C-54 aircraft were assembled and delivered from this airport. The plant and taxiways covered I,371 acres and the facilities, less machinery, were valued at $35,824,000. The plant was evacuated by Douglas in October 1945. After the members of the Committee agreed on its selection, negotiations were immediately started with the federal government. On March 22, 1946, the City of Chicago acquired 1,080.61 acres of the 1,371 acres. This tract included one small hangar on the south side and one lean-to building. The assembly plant and the other buildings were retained by the military. In 1949, the name Chicago Orchard Airport (Douglas) was changed to Chicago-O'Hare International Airport, in honor of "Butch" O'Hare, the World War II ace from Chicago.

By 1958 the plans for the enlargement and improvement of Chicago-O'Hare International Airport, compiled by various engineering firms, were now ready. A revenue bond issue was proposed in the amount of $120 million. The arrangement for repayment of the revenue bonds was unique in that they were underwritten by the airlines and would be paid off by them over a period of years. Further, the airlines agreed to pay the

7. Aerial View, January, 1973
The world's busiest airport sees 90,000 passengers each day.

8. O'Hare Dedication, March 23, 1963
President John F. Kennedy said "It is an extraordinary airport, an extraordinary city . . . "

9. O'Hare Tower, 1972
The shaft of the control tower is shown silhouetted against the O'Hare International Tower Hotel.

All photographs are on file with the Chicago Historical Society

8

9

maintenance and operating costs of the entire airport, which completely relieved the City of any expense to taxpayers.

On March 23, 1963, O'Hare Airport was dedicated by President John F. Kennedy. In his remarks at the dedication he said, "There is no other airport in the world which serves so many people and so many airplanes," and he added "This is an extraordinary airport, an extraordinary city and an extraordinary country, and it could be classed as one of the wonders of the modern world."

Today, ORD on ticket and baggage identification, an abbreviation for Orchard, reminds travelers of the early, modest origins of the world's most magnificient airport.

10

10. Control Tower, November, 1972
The world's only transparent radome sits 200 feet in the air atop the beautiful control tower, focal point of O'Hare International Airport.

11, 12. Hotel, 1973
The O'Hare International Tower Hotel is the largest, most unique airport hotel in the world. With 979 rooms, the hotel has seven restaurants, a block long shopping arcade, 83 conference and banquet rooms, and a large collection of 156 contemporary art works commissioned especially for the hotel. The spacious two story lobby includes 24 planted trees, 15 feet high.

13. Christmas at O'Hare, 1962
Terminal view of passenger traffic during the holiday season.

11

12

13

Merrill C. Meigs Field

Located on Chicago's lakefront, Meigs Airport offers unmatched convenience for the small commercial planes with passengers and cargo bound for the Loop. Meigs Field still remains the closest situated airport to a city central area of all the close-in airports in the United States. In addition, this geographical location is enhanced by its proximity to McCormick Place, Chicago's huge exposition hall and convention center.

Built on Northerly Island, part of the site for the 1933 World's Fair, construction was finished on this unique lakefront airport in 1948. To get the field ready for operations, it was enlarged by pumping sand fill on the east and south sides and constructing a paved runway together with taxiways and parking areas for planes. A maintenance and tower building and an administration and terminal building were also constructed. Runway lights, beacons and other necessary field lighting were installed. During the field's first month of operation there were 968 airplane operations, carrying 1,936 passengers.

On June 30, 1949, by action of the City Council, the lakefront airport was named in honor of Merrill C. Meigs, a pioneer aviation enthusiast. Today, Meigs Field is one of the world's busiest single runway commercial airports.

14. Rescue Station, 1973
Meigs Field Rescue Station offers a new dimension in fire rescue facilities. Located at Meigs Field Chicago's lakefront airport which offers unmatched convenience for small commercial planes with cargo and passengers bound for the Loop. The new rescue station will cover 10,000 square feet housing a first aid station, three helicopters, two fire trucks, a boat dock and administrative offices. Fifteen men will man this unique airport and lake rescue facility when completed in 1973.

15. Terminal Interior, 1972
Looking across the lagoon from inside the Meigs Field terminal building, the traveler sees Soldier's Field and to the right the Sears Tower is visible under construction.

16. Plane Holding Area, 1972
Small craft wait adjacent to the terminal building with Chicago's skyline in the background: from the left are the Prudential Building, the Standard Oil Building under construction, the Hancock Building and on the far right the Lake Point Tower apartment building.

17. Meig's Field Aerial, 1972
Meig's Field, located on Northerly Island, is partially visible in right hand portion of picture looking across Burnham Harbor and above Grant Park. The Central Water Filtration plant is on the horizon.

All photographs are on file with the Chicago Historical Society

14

15

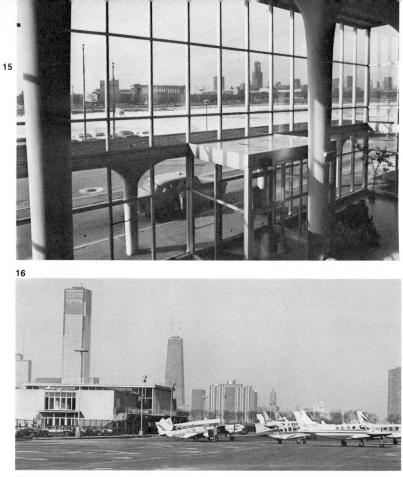

16

17

Beautification 14

Buckingham Fountain   1973
The Chicago skyline rises behind the Buckingham Fountain, the focal point of Grant Park. Built in 1927 on landfill along the lakefront, the fountain was a gift of Ms. Kate Buckingham in memory of her brother Clarence Buckingham, a former director of the Art Institute. Private donors, working together with municipal organizations have served Chicago's beautification programs well over the years.

The Need

Thinking of public works, a Chicagoan envisions enormous filtration plants, great bascule bridges and a myriad of engineering feats. Hardly anyone thinks of beautification.

Yet beautification is one of the most important aspects of public works. Cooperation between municipal and community representatives has transformed derelict vacant lots in highly populated neighborhoods into welcomed adventure-vestpocket parks; parkways and medians have become shaded promenades and plazas which have enhanced the environment of the respective neighbors.

As our cities become more densely populated, and individuals find themselves impinging on each other with greater frequency and intensity than in the past, human tensions rise, dirt and grime accumulate, and beauty indeed becomes a scarce commodity. And just as all public needs become public works in a well-managed urban society, so beautification has become a more important addition to the responsibilities of the Public Works Department.

The new thrust in beautification has had many forms:

- Vestpocket playgrounds in excess public rights-of-way
- Downtown plazas
- Riverfront improvements
- Landscaped bus stops and median strips
- Play lots and swimming pools adjacent to public buildings
- Neighborhood public facilities and school grounds
- Neighborhood block improvements
- Historic preservation

Beauty, like virtue, is said to be its own reward. Improving the visual quality of our neighborhoods is important, but is only one of the goals of the program. To develop a sense of identity and personal worth and an ability to cope with at least some of the evident urban problems, is the ultimate hope and aim of this program.

1. Drexel Blvd, 1972
With age and changing times, the parkway of this 200-foot wide street fell into neglect. Realizing the value of this priceless open space in a neighborhood of ever increasing density, a major rehabilitation project added eight plazas between 40th and 47th Streets, with shading Honey Locusts, Green Ash, Red Oak and Sycamore trees.

2. Drexel Blvd., 1892
Designed by the renowned architect, Frederick Law Olmstead, the mile long median on Drexel Blvd. made this area one of the most gracious of neighborhoods.

All photographs are on file with the Chicago Historical Society

Neighborhood Improvement

With regard to the quality of life, the Comprehensive Plan for Chicago states that as one of the strategic objectives: "Neighborhoods that are attractive to families with growing children as well as young unmarried people and older couples, will be created and retained." The plan focuses on those things which can be done now to have the greatest beneficial impact on the quality of life in Chicago immediately as well as in the long run.

In this spirit, landscape architects and engineers have worked together with professionals of all disciplines to create improved surroundings for people in all parts of Chicago. Through cooperation with Model Cities Environmental Coordinators, programs were developed to improve the visual fabric of those target areas.

On the Near North, several triangular street islands have been landscaped making use of multi-level and circular patterns to relieve the bleak, hard character of the pavement. In the same area, special block treatment has improved residential areas, particularly those where the trees had been destroyed by Dutch elm disease some years ago. For example, the solid architecture of Lakeside Place at Sheridan Road represents a uniquely strong residential block. Trees and sod were planted while special consideration was given to defining the block entry area to help reinforce residential identity.

Schools have been landscaped with regard for the intensive use these areas receive. At the Shakespeare School, brick work has been used to define main pathways in the previously unrelieved concrete expanse. Seating areas have been provided and appropriate trees and shrubs added.

Bus stops have also received special attention with appropriate landscaping, seating, pathways and in some cases canopies. Median strips have been cleared of litter and landscaped between 40th and 47th Street on Drexel Boulevard. This grand boulevard of horse and carriage days, once suffering from old age and neglect, offered priceless open space in a high density neighborhood. Fresh plantings, and imaginative sitting areas in this case, revitalize the area.

3. Shakespeare School, 1972
Reading, 'Riting and Rejuvenation are the three "R's" at Shakespeare Elementary School at 46th and Greenwood. Angular planting beds with varied trees and shrubs plus added seating facilities create an inviting environment in this busy school parkway.

4. Greenwood and 65th Street, 1972
Parkway landscaping with sod and shade trees can greatly enhance a residential block. At certain intersections, special emphasis is directed toward defining block entry. In this case, rustic wooden posts and hanging chains lend strength and style to the entrance.

5. 55th and Archer Avenue, 1972
Contour landscaping offers visual relief in a predominately flat city like Chicago. This median island invites pedestrians to rest and enjoy a moment's repose.

All photographs are on file with the Chicago Historical Society

4

5

215

Downtown

Following the riverfront for a block between Clark and LaSalle on Wacker Drive is the recently opened Riverfront Plaza. The split-level landscaped plaza offers the pedestrian a moment's rest from the fast pace of the central business district. Along the esplanade on Wacker Drive are two balconies overlooking the river with benches, potted trees and plants. The lower level has a serene cosmopolitan atmosphere. Trees, shrubs, inlaid brick and numerous benches give the plaza an excellent reputation as an informal luncheon stop for surrounding employees and a rest area for weary shoppers.

LaSalle Street is the financial heart of the city; 30,000 pedestrians per day travel each block of this district. To ease the glaring reflection of concrete and the monotony of building after building, boxed trees and planters were incorporated along the LaSalle Street sidewalks. An element of aesthetic refreshment for the harried pedestrian is offered by these new rows of colorful trees and plants.

Other downtown plazas, parks and beautification projects are in the planning stage: the Illinois Central River-Esplanade, Michigan to the Outer Drive; Heald Square at Wabash and Wacker; Benton Place and State Street; Lower Wacker Drive at Lake to State Street.

6. Riverfront Plaza, 1972
The LaSalle River Plaza on the riverfront between LaSalle and Clark Street is a split level landscape plaza offering the pedestrian a moment's rest from the fast pace of the central business district. Along the esplanade on Wacker Drive are two balconies overlooking the river, with benches, trees and plants. The unusual beauty and functional excellence of this park resulted in the city being named as the First Place Winner: United States Department of Transportation "The Highway and its Environment" award competition, 1972, in the Multiple Use of Urban and Rural Right-of-Way category. The river plaza lighting was also judged outstanding in visual performance and was awarded the Chicago Lighting Institute Award of Merit.

7. Michigan Avenue, 1973
Chicago's Public Works took advantage of a street widening project along Michigan Avenue to redevelop the Promenade. Exposed aggregate gives texture to the sidewalks and planters. Attractive light fixtures for both pedestrian and vehicular traffic were judged outstanding in visual performance and awarded the Chicago Lighting Institute Award of Merit.

8. Water Tower Park, 1973
In the heart of the busy shopping district on fashionable North Michigan Avenue is this small, restful park at the foot of the famed water tower.

All photographs are on file with the Chicago Historical Society

Creative Adventure Playgrounds

In earlier times, beautification and park improvement usually implied the acquisition and development of large land areas. Today, the so-called vest pocket parks are gaining favor. Located on excess expressway rights-of-way, vacant lots under elevated rapid transit lines and adjacent to public buildings, such parks are within walking distance for neighborhood families. Teams of engineers and landscape architects, working together with sociologists, psychologists, and urban scientists have developed the concept of the creative-adventure-playground, which is essentially, a method of making use of small areas to meet the special needs of children of all ages. In this way, the disappearance of major land areas is in part compensated for by the contemporary innovation of interdisciplinary team work.

Planning the child's play is one way society prepares the child for participation in the adult world. In crowded urban areas of rampant social problems, constructive play can be a valuable tool in aiding the child toward responsible adulthood.

Unfortunately, many playgrounds could not be more hostile than if they had been expressly designed for the purpose of preventing play. The unbroken expanses of concrete and asphalt punctuated with a few forlorn pieces of so-called play equipment are a tribute only to the "ease-of-maintenance" philosphy of our age, but little else.

By contrast, the creative-adventure-playground concept makes use of a small group of varied but related elements specifically designed to meet the highly complex needs of the growing child. The elements of the park are so arranged that the child may choose to play alone and still feel a part of the larger group of playground children. If large enough, the play area should have a series of activities from simple to complex in a series of manageable steps. In this way the older children provide models for younger ones but the initiative remains with the individual. To recognize that people share common goals and to learn to work together toward these goals is part of growing up.

Where possible, play areas are divided into two zones. One zone emphasizes physical activities including all elements

9. Caldwell and Landers Park, 1972
Creative adventure playgrounds, such as this award winning vestpocket park near the Edens Expressway, epitomize a new direction for Chicago playgrounds, making use of a small group of varied but related elements specifically designed to meet the highly complex needs of the growing child.

10. Boys at Play, 1972
The Caldwell-Landers expressway park offers an effective play area. The park supplies a series of activities which range from simple to complex. In this way, the older children provide models for younger ones but the initiative remains with the child. Vest pocket parks throughout the city have won both regional and national awards. The U.S. Department of Transportation presented the Highway Beauty Award for Outstanding Example of Multiple Use Urban and Rural Highways for the City's first vest pocket park at 18th and Union Avenue near the Dan Ryan Expressway.

All photographs are on file with the Chicago Historical Society

important to a growing child: running, jumping, sliding, crawling, climbing, and balancing. Most events are usually structured so that the child may proceed from one type of activity to another. The second zone is for creative play: digging, building and playing in water enables the child to interact with his environment. The activities in both zones should offer a variety of challenges from things that young children can easily master to those requiring the skill and agility of older children.

In practice, with the small and odd-shaped excess rights-of-way lots available, some compromises must be made. Dual-use facilities are helpful in extending the activity range. A multi-leveled spray pool, for example, can become an interesting climbing structure for small children when the water is off; e.g. Larrabee and Armitage Avenue. Sunken basketball and volleyball courts can become skating rinks in winter, e.g. 18th and State Street. A brick circular tiered seating structure around a spray pool can function as an amphitheater when the water is off, for storytelling or climbing games, e.g. Caldwell at Landers.

Because limitations in space prevent introduction of as many types of activities as might be desired in the vest pocket parks, extensive use is made of free-form structures which the child can use to create whatever his imagination directs. Limbs of trees, placed in sand and stripped of their bark, structured mounds, wooden platforms all serve a multi-faceted range of games. In Chicago, free-form wooden structures have been important elements of expressway parks at Caldwell and Landers (Edens Expressway), at Avondale and Mozart and also at Wood and Avondale (Kennedy Expressway). Once inside, alongside, underneath or on top of these wooden structures, children will find a fertile environment for creative play.

A sense of secrecy permeates intensive play and is essential to it. Therefore, care is taken in all park areas to place seating for parents out of sight of the child by use of landscape screening but in sufficiently close proximity that the parent can quickly reach the child if serious difficulties arise, or in the event the child needs reassurance or perhaps wishes to demonstrate a new skill. The intensive use of these new playgrounds is convincing evidence of their need and acceptance.

11. Girls in Vest Pocket Park, 1972
What may appear as a pile of logs to adults is a land of fantasy for children at play. Wooden free-form structures become space ships, mountains, fire engines or whatever the child's imagination directs.

12. Larrabee Fire Station Park, 1972
Vest-pocket parks offer neighborhood children a unique series of attractive and challenging activities. The creative adventure playground concept makes use of a small group of varied but related elements specifically designed to meet the highly complex need of the growing child. In this park, one zone of play offers all the important elements to emphasize physical activities, such as, running, jumping, sliding, crawling, climbing and balancing. A second zone is for creative play providing a place for digging and playing in water, as shown in this well-used spray pool. Small excess land areas adjacent to public buildings are being converted throughout the city into creative adventure playgrounds for neighborhood families.

All photographs are on file with the Chicago Historical Society

11

12

Public Facilities

Fire stations, police stations, ward yards, libraries and health centers were once treated as simply utilitarian structures, of purely functional intent and without architectural continuity to any particular neighborhood. Fire stations were usually identical in all neighborhoods. Landscaping, if existent, was usually confined to a row of uniformly spaced trees.

By contrast, today's architects design the public facilities with a view toward harmonizing with the other structures in the neighborhood. Such buildings now become dual-purpose projects, providing the needed public facility and a neighborhood recreational area. Landscaping and comtemporary fencing is used to screen unsightly equipment areas and parking lots. Entrance courtyards, atrium gardens, bus-sitting areas, pools and play yards, all with convenient and attractive planters and trees make these public facilities welcome additions to the community for the people who live and work there.

13. Forestry Building December, 1972
Attractive landscaping enhances even in wintertime. This building is located at 4931 South Union Avenue. It was completed shortly before this photograph was taken.

14. Community Play Lot, 1972
The Cabrini-Green play lots were designed with a view to heavy use. These rugged and durable structures appear dwarfed from the roof of the multi-story apartment dwelling which the playlot serves. Recognizing that planning the child's play is one way society prepares the child for participation in the adult world, constructive play can be an effective tool in aiding the child toward responsible adulthood.

15. Fire Station Pool, 1972
Happy shouts and screams rise above the waves and splashes of the children at the Fire Station pool on 6011 South Central Avenue. Firemen and Policemen help manage these pools by serving as lifeguards, swimming instructors and doing other sundry tasks during their free time.

13

14

15

Historic Sites

Preparation for the future must also include preservation of the past. Pullman Park at 111th and Cottage Grove is the first historical beautification project coordinated by the Department of Public Works. George Pullman, inventor of the sleeping car, built what he hoped would be an utopian, workingman's community for his employees. Today, many of Pullman's 19th Century Gothic and Queen Ann structures are preserved in their original style, and have become private dwellings. Although Pullman's community fell short of his utopian goals, the town survives today as a state and city Historical Site and has been nominated as both a City and a Federal Landmark.

The modest Pullman Park faces historic Hotel Florence. Previously surrounded by a traffic circle the small plaza served mainly as a pathway for pedestrians. Working together with the Pullman Park Civic Organization, the City revamped the area, consolidating the circle with another open space to the side and eliminating the circular movement of traffic about the park. Four paths converge at the central plaza where large circular elements make for a casual park setting, taking advantage of existing lawns and trees.

Particular care preserved a small stand of original Ginkgo trees, a very slow growing species and the world's oldest variety of deciduous tree. Restoring the charm and dignity of this unique pedestrian mall has revitalized the area for picnics and other festivities.

Improving the quality of life throughout Chicago by means of beautification and recreation is one goal of these continuing efforts. The broader aims and objectives of this work strive to arouse community interest, to create a sense of neighborhood and individual identity, to implant an enjoyment of natural and recreational elements, and to initiate a vigorous chain of public and private environmental improvements bringing beauty and a sense of fulfillment to our people.

16. Pullman Park Plaza, 1972
Across from historic Hotel Florence is the Pullman Park Plaza. Surrounded by benches, the center of the plaza contains a flower bed and markers that give historic recognition to the famed Pullman community. Pools of radiating brick make a free-form clover-leaf around the flower bed. A walkway from Cottage Grove Avenue and its corner bus stop goes through the park.

17. Stockyard Entrance
Built in 1865, the Union Stockyards moved Chicago's packing industry to a 175 acre location then four miles south of the city where one third of all slaughtering in the West took place. When refrigeration was introduced in 1869, the scope of activity widened to make Chicago the livestock center of the world, providing employment for thousands of unskilled immigrants arriving in Chicago. With decentralization brought on by technological changes, most of Packingtown's great plants began relocating by the 1950's and the yards closed after a century of use. The gates have been designated as a landmark and will be the site of a Public Works beautification project in 1973.

18. Glessner House, 1886
Shown in final construction, this historic residence was one of the last works of architect Henry Hobson Richardson. This landmark is to be landscaped under a public works improvement project. The residence is located at 1800 South Prairie Avenue, once the most fashionable of streets. John Glessner was one of the founders of International Harvester Company.

19. Interior Courtyard, 1973
In contrast to the fortress-like granite exterior, the interior courtyard is scaled to domestic needs with picturesque features.

All photographs are on file with the Chicago Historical Society

16

17

18

19

225

Chronology of Public Works Officials Appendix I

Chicago's first public officials were those elected to the Board of Trustees. Chicago became the seat of justice for newly formed Cook County. These elected officials in turn appointed public works commissioners. When Chicago became a city in 1837, the elected mayor acted as the head of public works with the aldermen performing as commissioners with certain exceptions. Later, in 1851 and 1855, the State appointed Boards of Commissioners, first for water, and later for sewerage; in 1861 these two boards were incorporated in a newly formed Board of Public Works. In 1876 the Department of Public Works was formed.

1833 Board President   Thomas J. V. Owens
Street Commissioner   Benjamin Jones, succeeded by O. Morrison, succeeded by S. W. Sherman

1834 Board President   J. H. Kinzie
Supervisor, Roads & Bridges   James W. Reed, succeeded by E. E. Hunter succeeded by J. K. Boyer

1835 Board President   H. Hugunin
Street Commissioner   John K. Boyer

1836 Board President   E. B. Williams
Street Commissioner   W. McClintock

1837 Mayor   William Butler Ogden
Aldermen Acting as Commissioners

1838 Mayor   Buckner S. Morris
Aldermen Acting as Commissioners

1839 Mayor   Benjamin W. Raymond
Street Commissioner   Charles M. Gray
Chief Engineer   Alvin Calhoun
Asst. Engineers   Charles Stanton, G. Chacksfield

1840 Mayor   Alexander Lloyd
Aldermen Acting as Commissioners

1841 Mayor   Francis Cornwall Sherman
Aldermen Acting as Commissioners

1842 Mayor   Benjamin Wright Raymond
Aldermen Acting as Commissioners

1843 Mayor   Augustus Garrett
Street Commissioner   Orson Smith

1844 Mayor   Alanson S. Sherman
Street Commissioner   Philip Dean

1845 Mayor   Augustus Garrett
Street Commissioner   Philip Dean

1846 Mayor   John P. Chapin
Street Commissioner   Charles Baumgarten
Committee of Streets and Bridges   Nathan H. Bolles, Joseph Wilson, Elihu Granger
Public Grounds and Wharves   Richard C. Ross, G. Manierre, Henry Magee

1847 Mayor
       Streets & Bridges
       Wharves & Public Grounds

James Curtiss
Charles McDonald, Wm. Snowhook, Thomas James
Peter Updike, Charles Sloan, Henry Smith

1848 Mayor
       Harbors & Bridges
       Wharves & Public Grounds

James H. Woodworth
R. J. Hamilton, George W. Snow, James Carney
W. B. Herrick, J. C. Haines, Robert Foss

1849 Mayor
       Harbors & Bridges
       Wharves & Public Grounds

James H. Woodworth
R. J. Hamilton, George W. Snow, James Carney
W. B. Herrick, J. C. Haines, Robert Foss

1850 Mayor
       Harbor & Bridges
       Wharves & Public Grounds

James Curtiss
Alexander Lloyd, Smith J. Sherwood, E. B. Williams
D. Richards, John C. Dodge, Isaac L. Milliken

1851 Mayor
       Superintendent of Public Works
       Harbor & Bridges
       Gas Lights
       Street Commissioners
       State Board of Water Commissioners

Walter S. Gurnee
Derastus Harper
Robert Malcom, Wm. Wheeler, Ezra Taylor
Chas. McDonnell, Isaac L. Milliken, Thomas Dwyer
Darius Knights, Jacob Doney, Wm. Justice
John P. Turner, President; Loomis, Haratio, and Alanson S. Sherman

1852 Mayor
       Superintendent of Public Works
       Harbor & Bridges
       Gas Lights
       Street Commissioners
       State Board of Water Commissioners

Walter S. Gurnee
Same as 1851
Same as 1851
Same as 1851
Same as 1851
Same as 1851

1853 Mayor
       Superintendent of Public Works
       Street Commissioners
       Harbor & Bridges
       State Board of Water Commissioners

Charles McNeill Gray
Derastus Harper
Darius Knight, Jacob Doney
Mitchell, Evans, Scoville
Same as 1851

1854 Mayor
       State Board of Water Commissioners

Isaac Lawrence Milliken
James H. Woodworth, President; John C. Haines, George W. Dole

1855 Mayor
       Superintendent of Public Works
       Street Commissioner
       Harbors & Bridges
       Gas Lights
       State Board of Water Commissioners
       State Board of Sewerage Commissioners

Levi Day Boone
Henry Fuller
H. B. Bay, J. Rehm, Alvin Salisbury
R. M. Hough, Elihu Granger, A. C. Ellithorpe
Ezra Taylor, Robert Foss, O'Neil
Same as 1854
W. B. Ogden, Pres., J. D. Webster, Sylvester Lind

1856 Mayor
       Superintendent of Public Works
       Harbor & Bridges
       Street Commissioners
       Chief Engineer
       Asst. Engineers
       Water Commissioners
       Sewerage Commissioners

Thomas Dyer
Elihu Granger
Samuel Myers, Sylvester Sexton, A. C. Ellithorpe
Peter Reis, Alvin Salisbury, Owen Dougherty
Ellis S. Chesbrough
Wm. Clarke, John Reid, A. F. Bradley
Geo. W. Dole, John C. Haines, O. Lunt
Wm. B. Ogden, President, J. D. Webster (Acting) Sylvester Lind

1857 Mayor
       Asst. Superintendent of Public Works
       Harbors & Bridges
       Gas Lights
       Water Commissioners
       Sewerage Commissioners
       Chief Engineer
       Asst. Engineers
       Street Commissioners

John Wentworth
Elias Shipman
Jacob Harris, George Sitts, John Dunlap
H. Greenebaum, Samuel Meyers, C. Wahl
Geo. W. Dole, John C. Haines, O. Lunt
Wm. B. Ogden, President; J. D. Webster (Acting) Sylvester Lind
Ellis S. Chesbrough
Wm. H. Clark, John Reid
D. C. Hawley, Wm. Dunn, Owen Dougherty

1858 Mayor   John C. Haines
Superintendent of Public Works   Reuben Cleveland
Harbor & Bridges   B. Carpenter, C. H. Abbott, A. Enzenbacher
Gas Lights   J. K. Bottsford, A. J. Wright, J. Comiskey
Chief Engineer   Ellis S. Chesbrough
Asst. Engineers   Wm. H. Clark, John Reid
Board of Water Commissioners   Noah Sturdevant, G. W. Dole, O. Lunt
Board of Sewerage Commissioners   Wm. B. Ogden, J. D. Webster, S. Lind

1859 Mayor — John C. Haines
Superintendent of Public Works — Reuben Cleveland
Harbor & Bridges — B. Carpenter, C. H. Abbot, A. Enzenbacher
Gas Lights — J. K. Bottsford, A. J. Wright, J. Comiskey
Board of Water Commissioners — Noah Sturdevant, G. W. Dole, O. Lunt
Board of Sewerage Commissioners — Philip Conley, J. D. Webster, S. Lind
Chief Engineer — Ellis S. Chesbrough
Asst. Engineers — Wm. H. Clark, John Reid

1860 Mayor — John Wentworth
Board of Water Commissioners — Orrington Lunt, President, Edward Hamilton, Benjamin Carpenter
Board of Sewerage Commissioners — Jas. D. Webster, President; Sylvester Lind, Philip Conley

1861 Mayor — Julian S. Rumsey
Board of Public Works Commissioners — Benjamin Carpenter, President; Frederick Letz, John A. Gindele
City Engineer — Ellis S. Chesbrough

1862 Mayor — Francis Cornwall Sherman
Board of Public Works Commissioners — Benjamin Carpenter, President; Frederick Letz, John G. Gindele
City Engineer — Ellis S. Chesbrough

1863 Mayor — Francis Cornwall Sherman (Start of 2 year term)
Board of Public Works Commissioners — John G. Gindele, President; Frederick Letz, Orrin J. Rose
Chief Engineer — Ellis S. Chesbrough
Asst. Engineer — William H. Clark

1865 Mayor — John Blake Rice
Board of Public Works Commissioners — John G. Gindele, President; Frederick Letz, Orrin J. Rose
City Engineer — Ellis S. Chesbrough
Superintendent of Streets and Bridges — J. K. Thompson

1867 Mayor — John Blake Rice
Board of Public Works Commissioners — A. H. Burley, John McArthur, W. H. Carter, W. Gooding, R. B. Mason
City Engineer — Ellis Chesbrough
Engineer Pumping Dept. — D. C. Cregier
Superintendent Streets and Bridges — J. K. Thompson

1869 Mayor — Roswell B. Mason
Board of Public Works Commissioners — R. Prindiville, W. H. Carter, John McArthur
Engineer Pumping Dept. — D. C. Cregier
Supt. Streets & Bridges — J. K. Thompson
City Engineer — Ellis S. Chesbrough

1871 Mayor — Joseph Medill
Board of Public Works Commissioners — W. H. Carter, President; R. Prindiville, J. K. Thompson, H. Bailey
City Engineer — Ellis S. Chesbrough
Engineer Pumping Dept. — D. C. Cregier
Supt. of Streets and Bridges — George W. Wilson

1873 Mayor — Harvey Doolittle Colvin
Board of Public Works Commissioners — R. Prindiville, President; J. K. Thompson, Louis Wahl
City Engineer — Ellis S. Chesbrough
Supt. of Streets and Bridges — George W. Wilson

1876	Mayor	Monroe Heath
	Public Works Commissioner	Monroe Heath (acting, 1876–1878)
	Supt. of Streets & Bridges	George W. Wilson
	City Engineer	Ellis S. Chesbrough
	First Appointed Public Works Commissioner, January, 1879	Ellis S. Chesbrough
1879	Mayor	Carter Henry Harrison
	Public Works Commissioner	Charles S. Waller (appointed May 19, 1879)
	City Engineer	B. Williams
	Supt. Streets and Bridges	J. J. Jones
1881	Mayor	Carter Henry Harrison
	Public Works Commissioner	Charles S. Waller
	City Engineer	Dewitt C. Cregier
1883	Mayor	Carter Henry Harrison
	Public Works Commissioner	Dewitt C. Cregier
1885	Mayor	Carter Henry Harrison
	Public Works Commissioner	Dewitt C. Cregier
1887	Mayor	John A. Roche
	Public Works Commissioner	George B. Swift
1889	Mayor	Dewitt C. Cregier
	Public Works Commissioner	W. H. Purdy
1891	Mayor	Hempstead Washbourne
	Public Works Commissioner	Louis E. Kuhns, (Acting)
1893	Mayor	Henry Carter Harrison, Sr.
	Public Works Commissioner	Hiram J. Jones
1893	Mayor Pro Temp	George Bell Swift
1893	Mayor	John Patrick Hopkins
	Public Works Commissioner	John A. Moody (Acting), John McCarthy
1895	Mayor	George Bell Swift
	Public Works Commissioner	William D. Kent
1896		Joseph Downey
1897	Mayor	Henry Carter Harrison Jr.
	Public Works Commissioner	L. E. McGann
1899	Mayor	Henry Carter Harrison Jr.
	Public Works Commissioner	L. E. McGann
1901	Mayor	Henry Carter Harrison Jr.
	Public Works Commissioner	F. W. Blocki
1903	Mayor	Henry Carter Harrison Jr.
	Public Works Commissioner	F. W. Blocki
1905	Mayor	Edward Fitzsimmons Dunne
	Public Works Commissioner	William L. O'Connell
1907	Mayor	Fred A. Busse (Start of 4-Year Terms)
	Public Works Commissioner	John J. Hanberg, B. J. Mullaney
1911	Mayor	Carter H. Harrison Jr.
	Public Works Commissioner	L. E. McGann
1915	Mayor	William Hale Thompson
	Public Works Commissioner	W. R. Moorhouse
		Frank J. Bennett, (1916) Charles Francis (1918)

1919 Mayor
Public Works Commissioner

William Hale Thompson
Charles R. Francis

1923 Mayor
Public Works Commissioner

William Emmett Dever
A. A. Sprague

1927 Mayor
Public Works Commissioner

William Hale Thompson
Richard W. Wolfe

1931 Mayor
Public Works Commissioner

Anton Joseph Cermak
A. A. Sprague
Oscar E. Hewitt (1933)

1933 Mayor
Public Works Commissioner

Frank J. Corr (Acting)
Oscar E. Hewitt

1933 Mayor
Public Works Commissioner

Edward Joseph Kelly
Oscar E. Hewitt

1935 Mayor
Public Works Commissioner

Edward Joseph Kelly
Oscar E. Hewitt

1939 Mayor
Public Works Commissioner

Edward Joseph Kelly
Oscar E. Hewitt

1943 Mayor
Public Works Commissioner

Edward Joseph Kelly
Oscar E. Hewitt

1947 Mayor
Public Works Commissioner

Martin H. Kennelly
Oscar E. Hewitt

1951 Mayor
Public Works Commissioner

Martin H. Kennelly
Oscar E. Hewitt
V. E. Gunlock (1952) George L. Dement (1954)

1955 Mayor
Public Works Commissioner

Richard J. Daley
George L. Dement

1959 Mayor
Public Works Commissioner

Richard J. Daley
George L. Dement

1963 Mayor
Public Works Commissioner

Richard J. Daley
Milton Pikarsky

1967 Mayor
Public Works Commissioner

Richard J. Daley
Milton Pikarsky

1971 Mayor
Public Works Commissioner

Richard J. Daley
Milton Pikarsky

A Chronology of Movable Bridge Openings Appendix II

Location	Date Opened	Location	Date Opened
Cortland Street	May 24, 1902	Roosevelt Road	Sept. 13, 1928
Division (Canal)	Feb. 1, 1903	LaSalle Street	Dec. 20, 1928
Throop Street	1903	N. Damen Ave.	Jan. 24, 1929
Randolph Street	Apr. 15, 1903	Clark Street	July 10, 1929
Division Street (River)	June 4, 1904	106th Street	Sept. 28, 1929
Loomis Street	Oct. 17, 1904	S. Pulaski Road	Aug. 22, 1930
Cermak Road	Nov. 1, 1906	S. Damen Avenue	Oct. 4, 1930
North Avenue	Sept. 21, 1907	Wabash Avenue	Dec. 20, 1930
N. Halsted (Canal)	Nov. 4, 1908	N. Ogden Avenue (River)	Dec. 9, 1932
Kinzie Street	May 10, 1909	N. Ogden Avenue (Canal)	Dec. 9, 1932
Washington Street	May 26, 1913	S. Halsted Street	Sept. 13, 1934
Grand Avenue	Dec. 30, 1913	N. Ashland Avenue	Aug. 20, 1936
92nd Street	Aug. 11, 1914	Lake Shore Drive (Canal)	Oct. 19, 1937
Chicago Avenue	Oct. 15, 1914	Lake Shore Drive (River)	Oct. 19, 1937
Jackson Boulevard	Jan. 29, 1916	S. Ashland Avenue	Apr. 17, 1938
Webster Avenue	Aug. 3, 1916	Torrence Avenue	Dec. 2, 1938
Lake Street	Nov. 6, 1916	S. Western Avenue	Dec. 17, 1942
Belmont Avenue	July 12, 1917	Canal Street	May 29, 1948
Monroe Street	Feb. 22, 1919	State Street	May 28, 1949
Michigan Avenue	May 14, 1920	N. Halsted Street (River)	Dec. 5, 1955
Franklin-Orleans St.	Oct. 23, 1920	Congress Street	Aug. 10, 1956
Wells Street	Feb. 11, 1922	Van Buren Street	Dec. 5, 1956
Madison Street	Nov. 29, 1922	95th Street	June 27, 1958
California Avenue	Oct. 1926	Harrison Street	Aug. 23, 1960
S. Cicero Avenue	Mar. 17, 1927	Northwest Expwy. Feeder	May 1, 1961
Adams Street	Aug. 26, 1927	Dearborn Street	Oct. 23, 1963
100th Street	Sept. 24, 1927	18th Street	Aug. 18, 1967

A Chronology of Expressway Opening Dates   Appendix III

From	To	Mileage	Date
Edens Expressway			
Lake Cook Road	Balmoral Ave.	13.0	12-20-51
Balmoral Ave.	Foster Ave.	.3	12-10-58
Foster Ave.	Kostner Ave.	1.4	10- 1-59
Calumet Expressway			
Kingery Exwy.	Sibley Blvd.	3.1	11- 1-50
Sibley Blvd.	130th St.	2.7	12-13-51
Steger Rd.	Sauk Trail	1.2	10-16-53
Glenwood-Dyer Rd.	Kingery Exwy.	3.1	7- 2-56
Glenwood-Dyer Rd.	Lincoln Hwy.	1.9	8- 1-56
Sauk Trail	Lincoln Hwy.	1.3	8-10-56
130th St.	107th St.	3.0	Fall 62
107th St.	95th St.	3.0	12-15-62
Kingery Expressway			
State Line Rd.	Calumet Exwy.	3.0	11- 1-50
Eisenhower Expressway			
Mannheim Rd.	First Ave.	2.5	12-21-54
Laramie Ave.	Sacramento Blvd.	2.7	12-15-55
Sacramento	Ashland Blvd.	1.7	12-15-55
Ashland Blvd.	Halsted St.	1.0	8-10-56
Halsted St.	Desplaines St.	.1	8-10-56
Desplaines St.	Canal St.	.2	8-10-56
Canal St.	Columbus Dr.	1.0	8-10-56
Howard Ave.	Mannheim Rd.	1.4	11-21-58
Madison St.	Hillside Ave.	.6	11-21-58
Central Ave.	Laramie Ave.	.5	1-29-60
First Ave.	Des Plaines Ave.	.9	7-30-60
Des Plaines Ave.	Austin Ave.	2.0	10-12-60
Austin Ave.	Central Ave.	.5	10-12-60
Lake St.	Soffel Ave.	.6	12-18-61
Soffel Ave.	Madison St.	1.7	12-18-61

From	To	Mileage	Date
John F. Kennedy Expressway			
(Airport Lead)			
Mannheim Rd.	Des Plaines River	1.3	9-27-60
Des Plaines River	Northwest Tollway	.6	8-31-60
Northwest Tollway	Foster Ave.	4.2	12-15-59
Foster Ave.	Kostner Ave.	2.2	11- 5-60
Kostner Ave.	Armitage Ave.	4.4	11- 5-60
Armitage Ave.	Ogden Ave.	1.7	11- 5-60
Ogden Ave.	C. & N.W. Railway	.5	11- 5-60
C. & N.W. Railway	Lake St.	.5	11- 5-60
Lake St.	Washington Blvd.	.2	9-30-59
Washington Blvd.	Congress St. Exwy.	.5	12- 4-58
Halsted St.	Orleans St. (Feeder)	.6	5-12-61
Adlai E. Stevenson Expressway			
Cook-Du Page Rd.	I & M Canal	6.5	10-24-64
I & M Canal	LaCrosse St.	3.5	10-24-64
La Crosse St.	Rockwell St.	3.0	10-24-64
Rockwell St.	South Quarry St.	2.3	10-24-64
South Quarry St.	Dan Ryan	0.3	10-24-64
Dan Ryan	Lake Shore Dr.	1.7	11- 1-66
Dan Ryan Expressway			
95th St.	71st St.	3.0	12-12-61
71st St.	63rd St.	1.0	12-15-62
63rd St.	Pershing Rd.	3.0	12-15-62
Pershing Rd.	Congress Exwy.	4.0	12-15-62
Dan Ryan Expressway—West Leg			
Halsted St.	95th St.	1.3	11- 6-63
127th St.	Halsted St.	4.2	10-24-67
Steger Rd.	167th St.	8.2	10-31-68
147th St.	127th St.	3.1	11-29-69
167th St. (175th St.)	147th St.	4.0	12- 5-70

Geographical Data

Location . . . . . Latitude, 41°50'N, Longitude, 87°37'W
Center of the City. . . . Approx. 3700 and South Honore
Area. . . . . 228.115 square miles
Lake Front (Miles of Shore Line) 29.0
Altitude (Feet Above Sea Level) 578.5

Population

City (1970 Census Final). 3,369,359
White (1970 Census Final). 2,207,767
Non-White (1970 Census Final). 1,159,190
County (1970 Census Final). 5,493,529

Weather: 1971

Average Temperature . . . . 60.9°
Warmest Day: June 28, 1971 . . . . 101°
Coldest Day: February 2, 1971. . . . . −9°
Snowfall (inches) 34.9
Precipitation (inches) 29.58

Government

Form . . . . Mayor Council
Council-Non-Partisan . . . . 50 Aldermen
Term of Office . . . . 4 years
Registered Voters (November 7, 1972) 1,714,641
Number of Precincts (November, 1972) 3,209
Town of Chicago Organized, Population (August 12, 1833) 350
First Charter with a legal limit of 1 square mile
Town of Chicago Incorporated, Population (February 11, 1835) 3,265
City of Chicago Incorporated, Population (March 4, 1837). 4,170
Second Charter - in order to increase size

Transportation Data

Motor Vehicles: 1971

Passenger 970,934
Transfers 137,330
Trailers. 656
Motorcycles 13,276
Horse Drawn 14
Trucks 67,037
Demonstrators 5,168
Total Licenses 1,194,415

Buses (CTA): 1971

Vehicles Miles 95,198,536

Rapid (CTA): 1971

Vehicle Miles 51,069,135
Passengers 103,499,016

Airports: 1971 3
Number of Plane Movements 928,484
Number of Passengers
Arrivals 16,186,027
Departures 16,137,093
Cargo Tonnage (pounds) 1,038,766,925

Traffic Facilities: 1971

Bridges
Moveable 55
Fixed (over waterways). 30
Viaducts. 74
Pedestrian Tunnels 27
Moveable Bridge Operations 45,377
Expressways:
Chicago (miles) 56.83
Streets:
City (miles) 3,681.54
Alleys (miles) 1,925.44
Street Lights (January, 1972) 174,792
Alley Lights (January, 1972) 45,616
Traffic Control:
Signalized Intersections (January, 1972). . . . 2,400
Channelized Intersections: (October, 1972)
Physically channelized 1,041
Paint channelized 377
Tows (1971)
Immediate 42,361
Abandoned 49,897
Miles of One-way Streets (October, 1972) 953

Water Facilities: 1971

Daily Per Capita Consumption, Chicago (gallons) . . 255
Daily Average Pumpage, Chicago (gallons)   858,910,000
Annual Pumpage, Chicago (gallons). . . 313,503,300,000
Meters, number in service. 163,988
Fire Hydrants 46,164
Water Mains (miles) 4,140.99
Miles of water supply tunnels under lake and land   72.6
Gross Cash Receipts (Water & Sewer) $71,004,306

Sewer Facilities (miles). 4,132.06

Building Statistics: 1971

Permits. 10,438
Value of New Dwelling Units $180,156,033.00
Dwelling Units Authorized by Building Permit. . . 10,696
Tallest Buildings:
Sears Tower . . . . . 110 Stories. . . . . 1,454 Feet
Standard Oil Building   80 Stories. . . . . 1,136 Feet

John Hancock Center   100 Stories. . . . . . 1,105 Feet
First National Bank . .   60 Stories. . . . . . . 841 Feet

Harbor Statistics (April, 1971 - December, 1971)
Navy Pier
   Overseas ship arrivals 80
   General cargo, imports (short tons) 130,230
   General cargo, exports (short tons). 66,471
Calumet River and Lake Calumet Harbor
   Overseas ship arrivals. 603
   General cargo, imports (short tons) 396,539
   General cargo, exports (short tons) 272,070
   Bulk grain exports (short tons). 1,538,992
Total import and export traffic (short tons). . . 3,474,621

Parks: 1971
Acres of Parks 6,440.14
Other Park Properties 550.96
Total 6,991.10
Number of Parks. 514
Number of Fieldhouses. 245
Stadia. 2
Number of Beaches. 30
Park Area - Shoreline & Harbors (miles). 38.22
Number of Golf Courses. 4
Number of Tennis Courts. 624
Number of Yacht Harbors 8

Number of Harbor Facilities (includes moorings)   3,272
Number of Swimming Pools
   Outdoor. 72
   Indoor 27
Attendance Grant Park Concerts in 1971 344,400
Capacity of Grant Park Garage 3,586
Attendance Soldiers' Field in 1971. 663,232
Parking Capacity Soldiers' Field (total all lots) . . . 4,977

Parking: 1971
Number of Parking Facilities 55
Capacity 11,274
Number of Parking Meters:
   In Facilities 1,564
   On Street 31,908
   Total 33,472
Meter Maids 45

Conventions: 1971
Number of conventions and trade shows 673
Number attending from out of town. 1,669,340
Delegates' Expenditures. $315,500,000

Vital Statistics: 1971
Deaths 36,991
Births. 66,711
Marriage Licenses (Cook County). 53,349
Divorces Filed (Cook County) 24,996

Index

Acknowledgments

Over the years the Department of Public Works Public Information Section has gathered stores of information in response to the questions of curious Chicagoans whose questions have ranged from when the first gas lights were placed in operation, to the capacity of the Central Water Filtration Plant. Much of this material has come from the engineering and architectural files of the Public Works Department as well as from other departments within the City and the Chicago Metropolitan Sanitary District. Important contributions were also received from other organizations: the International Harvester Company, the Chicago Tribune, Glessner House, the Oak Park Library, the Chicago Association of Commerce and Industry, the Chicago Transit Authority and the Chicago Historical Society. Books and periodicals were also an important source of information. The Journal of the Proceedings of the City Council of the City of Chicago has been published continuously since June, 1858. Prior to that time, these proceedings were published on Mondays in local newspapers. Public Works information also appeared in the City Directory before publication of the departmental annual reports which began in 1876. Special reports and books used included the *Straightening of the Chicago River,* published by the City of Chicago in 1930; *The Special Commission Chicago Drainage Channel,* published in 1900; *Drainage Channel and Waterway,* by G. P. Brown, published by R. R. Donnelly and Son, in 1894; *Chicago's Highways Old and New,* by M. M. Quife, 1923; *Seven Days in Chicago,* by J. M. Wing and Co, 1877; as well as several newer books: the exhaustive study, *Chicago: Growth of a Metropolis,* by H. M. Mayer and R. C. Wade, Finis Farr's *Chicago,* which provided the inscription for this work, and *Is There Only One Chicago?* by Kenan Heise. All photographs, in addition to those supplied by the Chicago Historical Society, are on file with the Chicago Historical Society for future reference and preservation.